The McLandress Dimension

John Kenneth Galbraith.

by Mark Epernay

The McLandress Dimension

WITH ILLUSTRATIONS BY

JAMES STEVENSON

HOUGHTON MIFFLIN COMPANY BOSTON

The Riverside Press Cambridge

1963

FIRST PRINTING

LIBRARY OF CONGRESS CATALOG CARD NUMBER: 63-19893

PRINTED IN THE U.S.A.

FOR PERMISSION to reprint previously
published reports on the work
of Dr. McLandress (and Mr. Wheat) I
am grateful to *Esquire* and *Harper's*.
M.E.

Contents

Introduction

McLandress the Man

WITH some modest satisfaction, I present in these pages the first comprehensive account of the work of Dr. Herschel McLandress. As in the case of any considerable scientific figure, there are differing views on Dr. McLandress. At the Harvard Faculty Club, the M.I.T. Faculty Club and even at the Cosmos Club, you will encounter both pro-McLandress factions and anti-McLandress factions. Some of the most trenchant debates in recent years at the Christmas meetings of the American Association for Psychometrics have been over McLandress and, above all, the McLandress conclusions.

But one thing is agreed. McLandress is a unique figure in our time. Even his severest critics in the scientific world

McL.

will concede this. "Something in the McLandress personality is different," a visiting Oxford scholar at the Institute for Advanced Study in Princeton observed not long ago. No one dissented.

I have been called the Boswell of Herschel McLandress. In a sense, I am. He has confided in me far more generously than in any other journalist. I have tried to requite this confidence with a genuine effort at understanding this scholar. It will be for the other disciples of McLandress to say whether I have succeeded. No one will think I failed for lack of effort and I hope no one will think I failed for lack of imagination.

It is not alone a masterful control of modern social science technique which lies back of the McLandress phenomenon. This is indeed important. So also are the deep insights into the fundamentals of human motivation as they manifest themselves in mid-century America. But the real genius of McLandress lies in his unexampled willingness to pursue his findings to their full and logical conclusions. Great men in our time — Henry Wriston, Christian Herter, John Rooney — have struggled with the organization of our Department of State. They have had less than success. It remained for McLandress to take the same data with which they worked (and some of their findings) and carry reform to its logical and inevitable conclusion. Many have seen the need to help those who wish to be known as responsible statesmen. But even the best coaching may not enable a man to find that precise formula which avoids the dangerous and damaging criticism which even those in the middle of the road may encounter from those who are on one side or the other. It was McLandress who analyzed the problem and then, accepting the full implications of his analysis, set up the system that allows every aspiring American to be, in his own way, a John Foster or Allen Dulles. Lesser men have probed gently into the American aristocracy. McLandress moved in and made the American system of social precedence a matter of arithmetic. Some have wondered if the minds of the great are focused with precision on their own personality. McLandress did not muse. He measured. Many have sensed the dangers inherent in the socialization of recreation. McLandress helped trigger a crusade to retrieve the values of individualism on the playing fields of the United States. Even though belatedly, it was McLandress who first saw how the enemies of Americanism, beaten on so many other fronts, would finally take over.

These are the reasons why, along with so many other good Americans, I am proud to call myself a McLandress man.

M.E.

The McLandress Dimension

The McLandress Dimension

THE McLandress Dimension, as it is known to scientists, is a new line of mensuration in the assessment of human behavior patterns. It allows the reliable sorting and classification of behavioral tendencies and it has already caught the attention of seasoned professionals as a possible way of predicting political and other career success. It owes its origins to the scientifically imaginative work of Herschel McLandress, former Professor of Psychiatric Measurement at the Harvard Medical School and now chief consultant to the Noonan Psychiatric Clinic in Boston. Because of his simple but searching insights, Dr. McLandress' work has long appealed to a small but devoted group of disciples, including a goodly number of informed and discerning laymen. With the McLandress Dimension, in the view of well-qualified observers, he is firmly destined for a place among the scientific and medical immortals. Certainly it will be among the best-remembered of his contributions.

The dimension along which McLandress has sought to measure human behavior is that of the individual's relation to self. The unit of measurement which he employs, called the McLandress Coefficient, reflects the intensity of the individual's identification with his own personality. No modern scientific tool is ever simple and the McLandress Coefficient — in scientific circles it is referred to as the McL–C (pronounced Mack-el-see) — is a thing of some complexity. But in essence it is the arithmetic mean or average of the intervals of time during which a subject's thoughts remain

centered on some substantive phenomenon other than his own personality. By way of illustration, a twenty-minute coefficient — a McL–C of twenty minutes — means that an individual's thoughts remain diverted from his own personality for periods of average duration of twenty minutes. A sixty-minute McL–C, a fairly large coefficient according to Dr. McLandress' researches, would mean that an individual's thoughts are diverted from himself for intervals averaging one hour. The McL–C, it should be noted, refers only to waking time. "The focus of the dream consciousness," Dr. McLandress has said, "is an important area of research, but it is not my present scientific preoccupation."

The McL–C for an individual is established by someone who is trained in Dr. McLandress' methods, and the individual may or may not know that he is being subject to psychometric measurement. Many of the ratings have been done by newspapermen who, after a brief but intensive period of training in Dr. McLandress' clinic, do the interviews under the guise of obtaining news. The subject is encouraged to talk with minimum restraint. By various depth perception techniques, including such simple indicators as substantive references to the first person singular, the intervals of thought-distraction are measured. They are registered by means of a recording stopwatch carried unobtrusively in the researcher's jacket pocket. Interviews are supplemented by what is called secondary communications research, which means, principally, a detailed study of the individual's oral and written expression — his books, articles, speeches, sermons, and interviews. Experience has shown that where published expression is adequate, the interview can be omitted and the coefficient established on the basis of such secondary material without loss of accuracy.

Although he is careful to say that his work is still in a preliminary state, Dr. McLandress has already established McL–C's for a sizable number of people. This is not a random sample; his concern has been quite frankly with people who are prominent in the political, scientific, academic, artistic, literary and business life of the United States and Britain. Early drafts of his manuscript, abstracts of which will appear in the autumn number of the *Journal of Psychiatric Measurement,* have been circulated for comment and criticism, and it is these that have provoked much of the recent discussion. When the full volume is published, Veritan Press, Inc., of Raleigh, North Carolina, will almost certainly have on its lists the first medico-scientific best seller since the famed Kinsey reports.

Interest will center, inevitably, on the coefficients that have been established for men and women who are prominent in public life. Dr. McLandress is careful to point out that these coefficients are "value-free." A low coefficient, one in the lower minute range, implies a close and diligent concern by the individual for matters pertaining to his own personality, but Dr. McLandress is careful to insist that this suggests neither superiority nor inferiority as compared with the individual with a higher coefficient. Nor can it yet be concluded that the person with a low rating is more effective or efficient than a person whose mental processes are less precisely concentrated. While Dr. McLandress occasionally hints at lines of thought emerging from his researches, he is careful to say,

"The task of the scientist is to classify and measure and, on occasion, to propose fecund lines of speculation but it is never his function to decide what is good or bad."

Many of the coefficients will not be thought entirely surprising. Thus, theater people have uniformly low McL–C's — the representatives of Broadway and Hollywood are nearly always in the minute range. Writers and playwrights, though with many exceptions, have higher coefficients than actors and actresses, and there are no significant differences between the latter. Both Mr. Arthur Miller and Mr. Tennessee Williams have a rating of thirty-five minutes. Mr. Gore Vidal, by contrast, has a rating of twelve and a half minutes. Among actors and actresses, Mr. Danny Kaye is something of a theatrical phenomenon with a McL–C of fifty-five minutes. Mr. Bob Hope's is eighteen minutes. At the other extreme, Mr. Mort Sahl has a rating of four minutes and Miss Elizabeth Taylor of three. By coincidence, Miss Taylor's coefficient is the same as that of Mr. David Susskind, the television impresario. This is impressively low. By further and quite innocent coincidence, Mr. Susskind's coefficient is the same as that of Mr. Nikita Khrushchev, whom he once interviewed on his television program. Mr. Khrushchev was rated from secondary written and verbal expressions and is the only Communist leader with a sufficient volume of personal expression to be handled in this way. No interview with Mr. Susskind was necessary.

Writers and journalists tend also to have low scores. At the upper extreme are Mr. Art Buchwald at two hours and Mr. Richard H. Rovere, *The New Yorker* writer and author of the recent volume of *The American Establishment,* with a rating of one hour and fifty-five minutes. Nearly all other writers and journalists are in the minute range: James Reston, ten minutes; Truman Capote, ten minutes; Dean Acheson, ten minutes; Vladimir Nabokov, ten minutes; Mary McCarthy, nine minutes; Ian Fleming, nine minutes; Kenneth Tynan, eight minutes; Max Ascoli, four minutes; Norman Cousins, three minutes; H. Trevor-Roper (the English historian) two and a half minutes. One writer and journalist conspicuously missing is Mr. Joseph Alsop. Dr. McLandress, in an amusing footnote, tells of his effort to interview Mr. Alsop in the course of personally establishing his coefficient. Dr. McLandress found himself deeply preoccupied with defending his methods against Mr. Alsop's strongly held views as to more appropriate procedures. Mr. Alsop also urgently advanced the hypothesis that men with high ratings would not face nuclear crises with adequate equanimity. As a result, the measurement of Mr. Alsop was never completed. Dr. McLandress hazards the guess that it is in the low minute range.

As might be expected, Dr. McLandress has established coefficients for a large number of his academic and scientific colleagues. For these, as also for ministers of the gospel, generalization is difficult — the range is from a few minutes to several hours. Thus, the Reverend Martin Luther King, Jr., has a rating of four hours; by way of contrast, both the Reverend Dr. Norman Vincent Peale and the Reverend Billy Graham turn up in the middle minute range. The nature of the pre-emptive character of spiritual preoccupation is, Dr. McLandress believes, a subject for further research. A similar dispersion characterizes the scientific community. Dr. Robert

Oppenheimer has a remarkable coefficient of three hours and thirty minutes, and Dr. McLandress suggests "as a further line of speculation" that this may well have been related to his problems as a security risk. "When a really first-rate mind is so divorced from self, it is certain to range rather widely. And we cannot be wholly surprised if this causes it occasionally to invade what many will regard as dangerous territory." Dr. Edward Teller, contemporary of Dr. Oppenheimer in the development of nuclear fission, has the much more conservative coefficient of three minutes, ten seconds.

In the academic world there is not only a wide dispersion in ratings, but also a considerable unpredictability. Dr. McLandress cites but tactfully refrains from giving the name of a Harvard Professor of Comparative Literature with a community-wide reputation for absentmindedness. On fine days he carries an umbrella; it is invariably left home in inclement weather. His Radcliffe students have not been the only ones to observe the occasionally embarrassing disarray of his attire. His McL–C was exactly two minutes.

Reflecting their strong interest in the McLandress work, which has had university as well as foundation[1] support, the Presidents of both Harvard and the Massachusetts Institute of Technology asked to be rated and will have their coefficients included in the forthcoming volume.[2] Both, incidentally, are a highly unspectacular forty-five minutes.

[1] Dr. McLandress acknowledges his indebtedness to the Ford Foundation, the Carnegie Corporation of New York, the Rockefeller Institute, the Overbrook Foundation, the Shelter Rock Foundation, Inc., the George M. and Pamela S. Humphrey Fund, and the Aadland Trust.

[2] Only a small sample of Dr. McLandress' coefficients, offered purely by way of illustration, are given here.

There is little doubt that it will be the McLandress ratings for political and other public figures that will provoke the most comment when they appear. And possibly with this in mind, Dr. McLandress has gone into greatest detail in this department. Political leaders, like actors, tend to low ratings. Some that are surprises at first glance seem much more reasonable on analysis.

The President of the United States, rated during a long and highly cooperative interview, has a McL–C of twenty-nine minutes. Prime Minister Harold Macmillan, who was similarly cooperative, has twelve minutes. In discussing the coefficients of these two political leaders, Dr. McLandress makes some allowance for the possibility of change. He hazards the guess that the President's coefficient may be higher than when he was serving as senator. The Macmillan rating, he feels, has recently gone down. Miss Christine Keeler, a somewhat casual acquaintance of Dr. McLandress from his visits to London, had a rating of two hours at the time of measurement.

The British Royal Family, much of which had to be rated from rather sparse secondary expression, provides few surprises. One is the coefficient of Antony Armstrong-Jones, now Lord Snowdon, who is far above all other members of the family with forty-eight minutes. Dr. McLandress, who is intrigued by the relation of royal lineage to McL–C, thinks that this may be the highest royal rating since Queen Victoria's consort, Prince Albert. People with a position in the court, as also in London and Washington society, have a uniformly low rating. Association with the great leads, evidently, to reflection less on the great associate than on the association. So thought returns to self. Two Washington hostesses of the Truman-Eisenhower era, Mrs. Perle Mesta and Mrs. Gwen Cafritz, who, surprisingly enough, caught Dr. McLandress' attention, are in the lower minute range. So were all Washington diplomats included in the study and Vice President Lyndon Johnson.

Rated from secondary oral and written communication — Dr. McLandress attaches considerable importance to the appearance of the first person singular and plural in such material — Winston Churchill has a coefficient of eight minutes. One of the few French leaders rated is President Charles de Gaulle. He has the surprisingly high rating (for a political leader) of seven hours and thirty minutes. Dr. McLandress, who has a high reputation in Paris medical circles and who has lectured at the Sorbonne and the Ecole de Médecine de Lyon, suggests that in de Gaulle's case the rating is misleading. The subject's thoughts are constantly on France and France has, in a sense, become the surrogate of his own personality. Thus, when he thinks of France, he thinks of himself and vice versa. Recalculated, with appropriate substitutions, de Gaulle turns out to have a McL–C of one minute, thirty seconds.

The McL–C of Churchill's old friend, Lord Beaverbrook, is two minutes. Lord Beaverbrook's coefficient is matched on this side of the water by an American elder statesman, Mr. Bernard Baruch. Speaking of Beaverbrook and Baruch, Dr. McLandress offers the thought that ratings decline with advancing age.

Other publishers are within range of Lord Beaverbrook, although there is none that matches his score. Mr. John Hay Whitney, owner of the *New York Herald Tribune,* has a

McL–C of one hour, twenty-seven minutes. (Mr. Whitney and Mr. Roger Blough of the United States Steel Corporation, one hour, thirty minutes, are both examples, according to Dr. McLandress, of men whose relatively high McL–C is associated with the diverting effect of a single strong external attraction. In the case of Mr. Whitney, this would appear to be the earnings statement of his newspaper; in the case of

Mr. Blough, it is the historic comments of the President of the United States on the steel industry.) The McL–C for Mr. Alfred Knopf is seven minutes; that of another publisher, Mr. Bennett Cerf, is one minute and seven seconds.

In the immediate field of American politics, only one member of the United States Senate has a McL–C of more than fifteen minutes. That is Senator Everett McKinley Dirksen, who has a McL–C of three hours, twenty-five minutes. In this connection — the question seems also to have arisen in the case of Mr. James Reston — Dr. McLandress has been asked if a subject sufficiently gifted in verisimilitude could contrive to give investigators the impression of a much greater McL–C than he really has. Dr. McLandress discounts the possibility. He attributes Senator Dirksen's politically high McL–C to an almost unique inability to divert his thoughts from the public interest.

Honors for the lowest coefficient in the Senate are evenly divided between Democrats and Republicans and the east and west coasts. This is the result of a tie between Senator Wayne Morse of Oregon and Senator Jacob Javits of New York, each with a coefficient of four minutes. A large number of the more devoted and diligent members of the Senate are within the four- to eight-minute range. Senatorial coefficients are also subject to some variation over time. Senators facing re-election had a lower rating than those recently returned for a six-year term.

Coefficients in the Executive Branch tend also to be low and to fall rapidly in the higher reaches of the civil service and political hierarchy. Dr. McLandress does not attribute this entirely to personal insecurity. In his view, men in senior positions in the government are generally more intelligent and thus have a more sensitive appreciation of the various contingencies and accidents that may await the person in public position in the United States. Coefficients are extremely low in the upper levels of the Department of State, the U.S. Information Agency and in sections of the Department of Agriculture. Ratings are also low in the White House.

High ratings were found in the Department of Commerce, the National Archives, and the Interstate Commerce Commission. Reflecting, according to Dr. McLandress, the natural concern of the judge with the problems of other people, the highest McL–C in the Federal Government was that of Chief Justice Earl Warren at four hours, thirty minutes. The lowest was that of Professor J. K. Galbraith, the then American Ambassador to India, at one minute, fifteen seconds. Noting the natural tendency of people to think that a diplomat's attention should be centered on his country rather than himself, Dr. McLandress warns once more against hasty conclusions. As instanced by General de Gaulle, there is an omnipresent tendency for people in important public office to confuse the two, and the tendency in the case of non-career diplomats is especially marked.

An incumbent and a onetime candidate for governor had the distinction of two of the three lowest McL–C's that Dr. McLandress had encountered at the time of his researches. The governor was Mr. Nelson Rockefeller of New York and one of the two men to break into what Dr. McLandress calls the "second range." Governor Rockefeller has a McL–C of forty-five seconds. This is very low, but ceases to seem so in comparison with Mr. Richard Nixon's coefficient which, at the time he was rated, was only three seconds. It should be noted, incidentally, that both of these ratings are based on a wealth of oral material and are thought by Dr. McLandress to be exceptionally reliable. A third public figure with a low McL–C is Mr. Lewis Strauss. First giving him a McL–C of thirty-eight seconds, Dr. McLandress re-evaluated him on the basis of his personal memoirs and put him in the high millisecond range.

These very low ratings for prominent political figures have led to the discussion of the advantages or disadvantages of a low McL–C for people seeking political preferment. In Dr. McLandress' view, concentration of attention on inward factors of personality is an advantage in politics and he adduces impressive empirical evidence to support his thesis. He has made an extensive case study of a New York congressional fight in 1960 between two closely matched contenders, Mr. John V. Lindsay and Mr. William vanden Heuvel. Equal in all other respects, Mr. Lindsay has a McL–C of fourteen minutes as compared with Mr. vanden Heuvel's of one hour and thirty-six minutes. Mr. Lindsay was the victor. Similarly in gaining office in New York State, Mr. Rockefeller was matching his 45-second McL–C against Governor Averell Harriman's 12.5 minutes. Governor Harriman was, of course, unseated. Dr. McLandress implies, and many will agree, that in the face of this evidence, undue significance cannot be attached to the last Presidential election when the relatively low-rated Mr. Kennedy nosed out the phenomenally low-rated Mr. Nixon. Other factors — the predominantly Democratic temper of the country, the close identification of the Democrats with the masses, the natural Democratic bias of the American newspapermen, the "me too" campaign of the Republicans — were all working for Kennedy. The almost total concentration of purpose implicit in his coefficient may well have been what enabled Mr. Nixon to do as well as he did. Dr. McLandress' informal advice to both political parties is to be extremely cautious about selecting any man with a coefficient of more than five minutes. In anticipation of the 1964 campaign, both parties are now quietly rating prospective congressional and gubernatorial — and in the case of the Republicans also presidential — candidates. Informed observers say, however, that this has not yet led to the exclusion of a large amount of potential talent.

The McLandress Solution

THE LARGE, handsomely attired man stopped talking for a moment, stretched his shoulders and lay back in his leather desk chair, his hands clasped behind his head. I found myself studying once more the strong features and the bushy eyebrows which seemed intended, somehow, to draw attention to the expanse of ruddy bald head above. My eye went past his shoulders to the glass doors and the expanse of green turf. I was reminded that my famous host was one of the few lawn-bowling enthusiasts in the United States — he had become a devotee many years before while pursuing postgraduate medical studies in Edinburgh. His voice brought me back to the room.

"So it all comes back to the two questions with which we started. What should I think? What should I say? If I have accomplished anything, it has been to give a little reassurance to the people who are struggling for answers."

He got up from his chair, squared his shoulders again and came round to the front of the desk. My eye took in the quietly graceful room, the single bookcase, the plain couch, the inlaid mahogany desk, the slightly formal Duncan Phyfish chairs, the Chinese rug, the Braque prints. Every reporter has had his great hours — over Germany in a Fortress, on the beach on D-Day, with MacArthur on the Yalu, asking questions in the Kennedy-Nixon debates. I could not be entirely sorry that mine had been in this spacious Edwardian house in Brighton, Massachusetts, in the company of the most famous of modern psychometricists.

The doctor took me by the arm and guided me through the study door. "After all you have heard, I am afraid you will find the physical scenery rather an anticlimax," he said. "But that is the sorrow of all who deal in matters of the mind. We have no cyclotrons, no space capsules, no gaseous diffusion plants, no Mach 2 supersonics. I wonder sometimes why the public takes us seriously at all."

We made our way along the passage to a back staircase and up to a spacious sunny room looking out on the shrubbery and back lawn. The ceiling and walls were covered with acoustic tile painted a warm rose. Around the wall on three sides were shallow cubicles, each with a formica-covered table, small shelf of books, single filing cabinet and telephone. There were perhaps a dozen in all. Only one of the cubicles was occupied — by a trim woman, late thirtyish with a sleek black hairdo. She was busy on the phone but, seeing us come in, beckoned us over, indicating that she would be finished in a moment. Above her head on the wall was a printed sign, TODAY, and below a typed paper with the words: "Bermuda: Young Corporation Presidents, National Goals. Dartmouth: Amos Tuck Alumni, Political Psychology. De Pauw: Chicago Execs, Philosophy of General Education. Denver: Chamber of Commerce, Theory of Modern Art." There were perhaps a dozen more such items on the list along with times of day. Besides, stenciled in permanent letters on the panel was a list of organizations and names together with telephone numbers: Council on Foreign Relations; Foreign Policy Association; Burns; McCloy; Ford Foundation; Hutchins; Wriston; Rovere; Rockefeller Foundation; Taft, Charles; Ward, Lady B.; Greenewalt; Killian; perhaps thirty others. Here and there a name — Rusk, Stevenson, Bundy — had a line drawn through it.

The woman put the phone on its cradle and rose to shake hands. "That was Bermuda," she said. "Poor connection. Young McAllister of Alpha, Inc. They are on national ethics of radiological permutation. He feels he has to participate."

"Yes, he should," said Dr. McLandress. "Sounds like one for Niebuhr."

"He isn't available today. I've put him on to Oppenheimer. Excuse me. That will be Arden House getting under way . . ." In a moment, she was concentrating again on her phone.

"This is a light day," said Dr. McLandress. "Come here in early June when every college in the country is having anywhere up to a dozen commencement seminars and you will find us really busy. Every phone manned and the calls backed up. An autumn weekend with the homecoming seminars can be pretty stiff too."

Another woman, younger, with red hair and a pleasant freckled face, came in and Dr. McLandress excused himself to have a word with her. My mind went back to our first interview. "To understand the problem I am trying to solve," he had said, "you must realize that the aspirations of the American people are entering a new and revolutionary phase. The Pilgrim Fathers measured people by their spiritual achievement — piety, chastity, adherence in general to the Ten Commandments. Then we moved to the age of material achievement and wealth became an index of accomplishment. The more a man had, the better he was, and at the apex was John D. himself. Maybe a rich man needed to call attention to his wealth — a big house . . . yacht . . . diamonds . . . old masters . . . philanthropy — but even the rich miser and the wealthy recluse were figures of real fame. It may not have been the most uplifting measure of accomplishment but it was certainly a convenient one. A man knew what he was worth; he had a pretty shrewd idea of the next fellow's assets. So his position in the community was wholly objective — a matter of accounting and arithmetic.

"Now we have come into a far more difficult period. I call it the age of responsibility. We measure a man by his ability to handle the economic, social, political, moral, ethical and religious problems of the time. Every day across the country there are dozens of conferences, seminars, forums, assemblies, workshops, task forces, panels and retreats all designed to test men's ability to take a responsible position on the problems that beset humanity.

"I do not say that wealth or income are unimportant. On the contrary, that is the heart of the problem. The country particularly expects the rich man to meet the test of responsibility. That is why it puts the Kennedys, Clarks, Lehmans, Rockefellers, Williamses, Harrimans, Wilsons, Bruces, Dillons, Biddles, Lodges, Weekses, Bowleses in positions of responsibility. But even if a rich man or a high-priced executive doesn't hold public office, he must show he can handle the big issues.

"Of course, there are a few holdouts — the executive who works an eighteen-hour day, goes in for golf and some two-handed drinking on weekends and gives a cheer for Barry Goldwater when anyone mentions politics. But even this fellow is only postponing the day of reckoning. One morning he will wake up president of the company, or break into the $100,000 salary bracket. Immediately he will have to know about the dynamics of Soviet society and the causes of the gold outflow. Then he will be knocking on the door downstairs."

Two more women had come in. After a brief word with each, Dr. McLandress came over to the window where I had been standing. "This took a bit of planning and I flatter myself it is pretty efficient. The standard stuff gives us no trouble at all — NATO, economic aid, collective bargaining, modern poetry, Lawrence Durrell. But increasingly the seminars are getting onto offbeat topics and the consultants are more of a problem. Even the most responsible scholars have their off days.

"We have tie-lines so that anyone who calls in is put right through to the consultant and our girls listen in. In this way they can catch any odd-ball idea. They don't interrupt, of course. But they call back afterward and tell the consultee what he should delete. It's a fairly foolproof system — or has been so far." Dr. McLandress held up two crossed fingers. "Out at Aspen last summer in a forum on history of religion, one of our clients got a statement from the Harvard Divinity School that was favorable to simony as practiced in the thirteenth century — essential for church revenue or something. He came out for it in the modern church. To make matters worse, he seems to have been mixed up as between simony and sodomy. No repercussions fortunately.

"Some will say that executives should stand on their own feet — that this coaching is wrong. In fact, we are only giving them a fair shake. We are the poor man's — or perhaps I should say the poor rich man's — foundation. You haven't forgotten what I told you about the foundations."

I had not forgotten. Dr. McLandress had called the modern foundation the clue to the new class struggle. They provide a few rich individuals with privileged access to the responsible ideas of the day and to a considerable extent the foundations decide what *is* responsible. The consequences are highly unfair. By all the rules, the Fords and the Rockefellers should now be slipping into obscurity. The Fords have only a little to do with automobiles. The Rockefellers have nothing to do with oil. Money is no longer by itself a source of esteem. Yet because of the Ford Foundation, the Rockefeller Foundation and the Rockefeller Brothers Fund, the members of these families grow daily in distinction. That is because what the Ford Foundation or the Rockefeller Brothers Fund say on a subject is important simply because they have said it. The Ford brothers or the Rockefeller brothers are bound to know in advance what their Foundations will say. As a result, their reputation for responsible statesmanship is unparalleled.

By contrast, the average rich man — the individual with a $200,000-a-year salary or $5,000,000 in bonds, stocks and real estate — cannot afford a Foundation or a Brothers Fund. At most he can get the part-time help of some impecunious professor who cannot be quoted in public. Yet this man must

also take responsible positions. He must participate in the seminars, attend the workshops, take his place on the panels.

If he is head of a very large company, he may be called to Washington. If it weren't for Dr. McLandress, he would be pretty bitter about the advantages of the very rich with their privileged access to the sound positions.

Dr. McLandress' voice recalled me to the sunny room. "Unless I'm mistaken, Nora here has one of our most common requests." One of the new arrivals, who was talking on the telephone, waved her hand over the back of her head in agreement and after listening for a moment, said, "Best of luck and be careful!" and hung up. A tall, intelligent-looking girl in her thirties, she rose from her chair and joined us.

"They are discussing China in Minneapolis. A vice-president of Federated Milling, Merrill Hansen, was just leaving and had to have the line."

"Federated Milling is a corporate client," Dr. McLandress explained. "We give service to any executive who needs it. What is it — the Walter Judd Far Eastern Forum?"

Nora nodded. "They are meeting at eleven, their time."

"To most people, China is a puzzling problem in responsibility," Dr. McLandress commented. "You can't be for recognizing Red China. That is politically impractical and still a little dangerous. But you can't advocate all-out support for Chiang. That marks you as a relic of the China Lobby. So the average executive doesn't know what to say."

I confessed that I was at a loss too and asked Dr. McLandress with whom Mr. Hansen had been put in touch.

"On a standard matter like that, we have the responsible answers right here. On China, we even give a choice. The preferred position is from *Prospect for America* — which, incidentally, is a publication of the Rockefeller Brothers and shows what it is to have a foundation." He picked up the still open book which Nora had laid beside the phone and showed me a circled passage:

> Toward mainland China, the alternatives of policy are, for the short run, lacking in creative possibilities. The value of diplomatic recognition and admission to the United Nations can be variously debated.
>
> What self-interest and enlightened policy do require of the United States at this juncture is a candid recognition of what Communist China is and where it is going. For too many Americans the assumption has seemed to be that China's absence from the United Nations could mean its absence from their minds.

"I think you can see that is a pretty responsible position. It doesn't propose any drastic action. It tells people the Chinese are here to stay. It urges serious thought. Of course we tell our consultees to put it in their own words."

I asked what the other position was.

"We like to have what we call the position of permissible originality — not for Mr. Hansen but for more thoughtful types. As I recall, Nora, it accepts the idea of eventual recognition but says that the Red Chinese must give up aggression, recognize Formosa, conciliate India and approach the free nations with clean hands."

Nora nodded agreement. "That's right. We no longer require them to renounce Communism."

"The China problem is a tough case of overlapping moderation but you see that with a little imagination, one can still get on very sound ground."

*

GIVE UP AGGRESSION
CONCILIATE
INDIA

RECOGNIZE FORMOSA

APPROACH
THE FREE
NATIONS
WITH CLEAN
HANDS

At one of our meetings, Dr. McLandress had explained to me the principle of overlapping moderation. It is the tendency for virtually all present-day propositions, when stated with sufficient moderation, to become internally contradictory. The inexperienced seminar participant finds this confusing for the contradiction is often fairly obvious. Dr. McLandress had given me a dozen or more examples, to wit:

1. The uncontrolled arms race is the gravest threat to the survival of mankind and we are deeply and responsibly concerned with the survival of mankind. However, as a serious practical matter, we cannot give up our deterrent power but must strengthen it.
2. The United States has a highly dynamic economy. However, the rate of growth is not satisfactory.
3. It is the task of the government to insure satisfactory performance by our economy. However, this should not lead to any increase in the already very large responsibilities of the state.
4. Capital and labor must be subject to restraint in their demands. However, anything that smacks of wage- and price-fixing is seriously inconsistent with the American system.
5. Fall-out shelters are an elementary precaution against the eventuality of nuclear war. However, it must be conceded that they do not offer any effective protection.
6. The United States is a deeply religious nation. However, the Supreme Court, in outlawing the prayer prescribed by the New York State Regents and in more recent decisions, has usefully reaffirmed the essentially secular nature of our society.
7. In dealing with the Berlin problem, we always stand ready to negotiate. However, we must recognize that any concessions will be taken by the Soviets as a sign of weakness.

8. Art is for art's sake but beauty is essential for a rational social order.
9. The foundation of the American society is the sanctity of the American family. However, it is a mark of maturity that we now take an increasingly liberal view of premarital and extramarital intercourse, consenting homosexuality, and nonlethal flagellation.
10. We have nothing to fear from a spiritually based materialism. However, it does have an immutable tendency to develop into a materialistically based spiritualism.
11. Crime and violence on television are damaging to the minds and morals of our children but any form of censorship is abhorrent.
12. The American image abroad must be improved. There must be nothing in this image-making that smacks of Madison Avenue.
13. World living standards must rise. This, however, is impossible because of the rapid rate of population increase. Population must be controlled. However, this encounters highly sensitive religious objections which, as a practical matter, must be respected.

I had confessed to Dr. McLandress that I found these contradictions puzzling myself and asked how they could be resolved.

"Your average seminar or workshop participant is helpless," he had replied. "But for the person schooled in responsible behavior, it is not so difficult. As in the case of China, your responsible man never gets involved with either of the main positions. Instead, he diverts discussion into some new and responsible channel. In that way, he gets credit for thoughtfulness and even originality and no one thinks him reckless or dangerous. We call this the technique of 'the third-dimension departure.' The foundations have done very good work along these lines. Sometimes we get help from politicians — the more scholarly Democrats are especially skillful. And we have the university statesmen. If a man has made a reputation for responsibility, you can be sure he has devised some very good third-dimension departures."

We took a turn around the room. The girl in the first booth hung up the phone and looked up. "I think you might have a word with Professor Kissinger. He is out of telephone contact again. A G.-M. vice-president named McArdle is in Santa Monica at the Civilian-Military Strategic Theory Workshop at RAND and needs a responsible position on the use of tactical atomic weapons in case of renewed fighting in Laos."

Dr. McLandress made a note. "I'll speak to him. Meanwhile, why don't you try Dean Acheson?"

Nora was reading over the phone again from the red, white and blue paperback of the Rockefeller Brothers Fund and when she had finished, Dr. McLandress took it out of her hand and pointed to the passage:

> Industry and labor should continue to seek out new production and construction methods to reduce costs and increase production as a positive approach against inflation.

"There you see the almost perfect third-dimension departure," he observed. "The question is what to do about inflation. That answer sidesteps all questions of price control or wage control and avoids saying whether labor or capital is to blame. It asks both parties to continue what it is careful to say they are already doing. So no one can think that the suggestion is at all radical. And it very subtly reminds people that this is a *positive* and not merely an ordinary or passive approach. You can see again what it means to have a foundation at your fingertips."

The girl in the next booth but one had a brown paperback in her hand. I leaned over to see the title — *The Report of the Commission on Money and Credit* of the Committee for Economic Development — and as I did so, her soft, precise, dictating voice came to my ear, ". . . no single economic goal can be wholly unqualified, because each may have to be sought subject to constraints imposed by other goals or at costs representing sacrifices, to some degree, of other goals . . ." She added, "Please be careful in changing the language not to change the meaning."

"Financed by the Ford Foundation and the Merrill Foundation," Dr. McLandress whispered. "David Rockefeller was a member of the Commission."

Our last stop was by the sleek, dark-haired woman who had come in first. She was reading from *The Report on the President's Commission on National Goals.* Dr. McLandress reached over her shoulder and ran his finger along a marked passage:

> In view of the complex interaction of arms control and national security, we must organize a major government effort for the study and analysis of political, military and technical issues . . .

"A competent third-dimension departure," said Dr. McLandress, "and one that had some very responsible thinking.

That study was financed by the Ford Foundation, the Rockefeller Foundation, the Alfred P. Sloan Foundation, the Falk Foundation, the Johnson Foundation, the Richardson Foundation, and the Carnegie Corporation."

The American Sociometric Peerage

ON FEW of his researches has Dr. Herschel McLandress, the great Massachusetts psychometricist, been quite so reticent as on those having to do with what he calls "the American system of social precedence." And he has never concealed the reason from his friends. "*Burke's Peerage* and *The Almanach de Gotha* were in the public domain," he has often said, "because that is where it paid the compilers to have them. My system is private for the same reason. Also, I need the money."

There have, in fact, been more than a few hints of the McLandress work on the American social hierarchy including the two substantial articles in *The Journal of Identity*.[1] And

[1] Vol. XI, No. 2 (January 1958). Pp. 76-96. Vol. XIV, No. 6 (June 1961). Pp. 455-475.

clients and patients have contributed to a general if somewhat guarded discussion of the work. Nevertheless, his decision a few weeks ago to talk freely about these investigations for the first time is a scientific event of first importance. This article is the first detailed exposition of the McLandress approach to the American aristocratic system. "You can thank," Dr. McLandress told me, "a certain mild affluence which has put me in a higher tax bracket than I find wholly comfortable. I must also lighten what is by way of becoming the most burdensome part of my practice."

What Dr. McLandress has done is to isolate the principles underlying the American system of social precedence — in a word, the American aristocracy — and to make a person's position therein subject to simple mathematical determination. He has also counseled an eager and growing clientele on how to advance their position. This service, incidentally, is not inexpensive. Dr. McLandress is still reluctant to talk about fees and so are his clients. However, a few years ago a major New York executive in the mass communications media field and occasional contributor to *The New York Times Magazine* and *The Yale Review* was involved in an income tax suit. Among the contested items, listed as a business expense, was a payment of $7,566.76 to Dr. McLandress.

Dr. McLandress is a stout defender of the social utility of his work. "There are no democracies," he told an interviewer not long ago, "only aristocracies that are ordered in accordance with different principles. Americans are as much concerned with prestige and position as any people on earth. More so, I think, for while the English are a little jocular about Norman blood, the rise of Lord Snowdon, life peers and the occasional earl who inherits from a job as lavatory attendant in Waterloo Station, we are still in the process of perfecting our system of social precedence. And it is right that we should. People need to know where they stand. The alternative to a well-defined social structure is not social equality but worried speculation by the individual about his position and this ends far too often in acute neurosis. I free the mind for better things. Naturally I get a lot of attention from ambitious people but I haven't heard that ambition is un-American."

It was the extreme complexity of the American social structure which defeated students prior to McLandress. Their approach had been what he calls "non-additive and one-dimensional" and the American system is complex and many-sided. Thus, scholars had assumed that prestige and social position are determined by one distinguishing claim to fame — by money, family, business success, political achievement, literary or theatrical fame, social distinction, behavioral notoriety or some other single factor. No way had been found to bring these to a common denominator — to equate the position of (say) the president of the Standard Oil of New Jersey with that of a leading Hollywood producer or the Senate Majority Leader. And prestige does not depend on position or accomplishment in a single field. As Dr. McLandress has shown, a great deal depends on the ability of an individual to combine accomplishment or seeming accomplishment in several of what in the McLandress jargon are called "Areas of Identification." The skill with which this is done must be measured.

In the mobile American aristocracy, it also makes a considerable difference whether the individual is rising — a "comer" — or whether he is stationary, or on the way down. Finally, in most fields a radical adjustment must be made in an individual's position on the day he is forced to affix the prefix "ex" to his name. The ex-Senator, the ex-corporation president or the ex-Hollywood star has, at best, only the pale shadow of his former grandeur.

The anchor of the McLandress system is what is called the Maximum Prestige Horizon — MPH for short. The Maximum Prestige Horizon shows on a scale from one to twelve the maximum prestige or distinction which a given vocation, avocation, area of literary or cultural achievement or other Area of Identification can confer on an individual. Current MPH ratings for a selection of Areas are given in the accompanying box. The word "maximum" should be carefully noted. It shows how high the individual can rise in the particular Area; in many instances this top score is achieved by only one or two individuals in the entire American community. Even the most prestigious people (as they are commonly regarded) in a given Area usually occupy positions below the maximum. Thus, by way of illustration, politics has an MPH of 12 reflecting the very considerable prestige of the President of the United States. Only the President has this top rating. The next highest score, that shared by Vice President Johnson, Senator William Fulbright, Governor Nelson Rockefeller and Adlai Stevenson, is only 8. (At times in the past the Secretary of State has also enjoyed this rating.) Cabinet officers (with the exception of the Postmaster-General), Mr. McGeorge Bundy, Under Secretary of State Ball, Senators Douglas, Clark, Javits and Humphrey and the Governor of California have a rating of 7. Except in the rare instances when an individual of exceptional energy or qualification has been able to bring special luster to his post, the ratings associated with the other political positions — midwestern governors, medium seniority members of the House of Representatives, southern Senators — are much lower. However, even these relatively low ratings are redeemed by certain adjustments to be mentioned presently.

Closely allied in modern times with politics is punditry — roughly speaking, a reputation for high authority on the critical questions of domestic and especially of foreign policy of the day. At the moment only one man, Mr. Walter Lippman, has the top rating for punditry of 9. (Mr. Joseph Alsop and Mr. James Reston are currently at 7; Mr. Henry Kissinger and Mr. John J. McCloy are at 6; Mr. David Lawrence and Miss Marguerite Higgins are at 4.) But the importance of punditry lies in the fact that it is open to all. Anyone who is seeking to advance his position can practice it and, with

MAXIMUM PRESTIGE HORIZONS

Area of Identification	*MPH*
Politics	12
Punditry	9
Theater (Hollywood)	9
Theater (Television)	8
Education (University)	8
Music (Popular)	8
Letters (Popular)	7
Publishing	7
Bureaucracy; public service	7
Science	7
Athletics	6
Labor Organization	6
Theater (Legitimate)	6
Philanthropy	6
Music (Serious)	6
Medicine	6
Economics, History, Sociology	6
Journalism	6
Military (Peacetime) (War: 10)	6

diligence or luck, improve his standing. The ambitious business executive, lawyer or man of wealth is almost automatically advised to write (or have written) a book or an article for *Foreign Affairs* on the future of NATO, the evolution of the Common Market, the role of private investment in economic development or, as an absolute minimum, he is urged to accept speaking engagements on some such topic as American responsibility in the current world crisis. Given the

MAXIMUM PRESTIGE HORIZONS

Area of Identification	*MPH*
Business	5
Painting	5
Architecture	5
Banking	4
Wealth (Established)	4
Religion	4
Wealth (New)	3
Law (Private practice)	3
Agriculture	3
Education (Other)	3
Patronage: arts, theater, ballet	2
Personal Beauty and Associated Accomplishments (Women only)	2
Masonic Order, Shrine, Elks, Odd Fellows, Rotary, Kiwanis, Kinsmen	1
Eccentricity	1
Hospitality	1
Sartorial distinction (Women only)	1
Horses	1

high MPH associated with punditry, even a modest performance will, after adjustment, contribute substantially to a man's standing.

Hollywood, which in the days from Mary Pickford and Douglas Fairbanks to Clara Bow and Lionel Barrymore may well have had an MPH above that of politics, has lost standing in recent years and is now only on a par with punditry. Only two people, Mr. Marlon Brando and Miss Elizabeth Taylor, currently have the horizon rating of 9.

The MPH for television, which has been rising, has not yet quite reached that of Hollywood. Since Mr. Edward R. Murrow left to become an important public official, no one has enjoyed the top rating. For others the ratings are highly unstable. The top figures of one season — the Godfreys, Wallaces, Sullivans — may have a rating that is barely positive in the next. By contrast, university education which has the same MPH, and where three college presidents — Dr. Nathan Pusey, Dr. Robert Goheen and Dr. Clark Kerr — are all at the horizon, has ratings that are highly stable.

The MPH's of other Areas of Identification are more or less self-evident. Since the age of jazz, popular music has had a high MPH; it still holds a slight lead over popular letters where the ruling personalities are now Mr. John Steinbeck, Mr. Edwin O'Connor and Mrs. Helen Gurley Brown. The MPH for publishing is 7 although not since the partial retirement of Mr. Arthur Hays Sulzberger has anyone held the horizon rating. Publishing, like punditry, is open to the well-to-do and ambitious but not otherwise talented man who

wishes to advance himself. Dr. McLandress encourages a fair number of his wealthier clients to consider the purchase of newspapers.

The MPH of the professional bureaucracy, which also includes unpaid but non-political public service, has an MPH of 7. Since the resignation of Mr. Robert Moses from his numerous positions in the New York State Government, the sole possessor of the top rating has been the United States Ambassador to Paris, Charles Bohlen. The MPH for science, which has been rising over the years, is 7 and here no fewer than eight men, led by Presidential Science Adviser Jerome Wiesner, are at the horizon.

At one time the MPH for organized athletics was only a little below that of Hollywood and, in their day, John J. McGraw, Babe Ruth, Jack Dempsey, Tyrus Cobb and Knute Rockne would all have been accorded the horizon rating. Now a man has nearly as much chance for distinction in biochemistry as in baseball and only Mickey Mantle enjoys as much primary prestige as Robert Oppenheimer and Jonas Salk.

In 1940, when Dr. McLandress established his first Maximum Prestige Horizons, that of organized labor was 10 and Philip Murray and John L. Lewis shared the top rating. Now the MPH for labor is only 6 with Mr. Walter Reuther and Mr. George Meany at the top. Mr. James Hoffa's rating is 4 and this seems not to have been appreciably lowered by his legal difficulties. Business, another Area of Identification which is in decline, has a current MPH of 5 and this is achieved only by Mr. Frederic G. Donner, the head of General Motors and one or two others. This means, in practical terms, that although Mr. Donner is the head of the nation's largest industrial corporation, he passes through airports, enters restaurants and goes to hotel desks without being recognized. As will be noted presently, we have here the principal reason why the successful businessman now resorts to punditry or, in the manner of Mr. George Romney or Mr. John Hay Whitney, to politics or publishing.

In the days of the elder Morgan, the MPH of banking was probably equal to that of politics. Now this is also in accelerated decline with a current horizon of only 4. No banker *qua* banker is known outside of his profession and here too it is taken for granted that members must resort to other prestige-building roles if they are to have appreciable precedence. The man of established wealth — the archetype is an Astor, Rockefeller, Mellon or Ford with no claim to consideration save his inherited assets — has also fallen on dark days. Indeed, an energetic and talented man has now as good a chance for advancement by becoming a major religious leader as the boy who relies only on birth.

Old-fashioned or conspicuous ostentation — the great house in Newport or Palm Beach — no longer confers distinction. Cultivated ostentation — broadly speaking, an intelligent patronage of the arts — has small but positive possibilities. It was part of the original genius of men like Mellon, Morgan and Frick to see at an early stage that a Rembrandt or a Rubens did far more for a man than a mansion.

Superior personal beauty and the normal accompanying accomplishments can add a measure of distinction to a woman but, unless associated with a motion picture or television career, it is relatively slight. The United States accords prestige to stars but not to good-looking women as women. Miss America must be able to compose music or recite poetry and she has only the most transitory fame unless she goes to Hollywood or develops an imaginative personal life. Sartorial and culinary excellence as well as professional eccentricity accord little scope as such; however, they continue to be slightly important for building up prestige in other fields. Even the most exalted positions in fraternal orders or service clubs do little for a man. Horses, once a prime source of prestige, are now barely positive.

The establishment of the Maximum Prestige Horizons, which has been done with no small precision, is an example of the ingenuity which Dr. McLandress has brought to psychometric and sociometric method. Over the years men and women in ever increasing numbers have been coming to Dr. McLandress to discuss ways of enhancing their personal position. Position, obviously, is a subjective thing — in the end it is what those most concerned with position think it is. So Dr. McLandress' clients and patients were, by self-selection, the people best qualified to judge where others stood. By penetrating deeply into the conscious and subconscious of his clients, he was able to determine the prestige which they associated with various Areas of Identification. He assigned a numerical value to this position. Thence by aggregation and averaging, he established the Horizons on what, obviously, is a highly scientific basis. The McLandress system has the further virtue of keeping both Horizons and personal ratings continuously abreast of the current prestige assessment. Each client helps to update the calculations. And, as ever increasing numbers have come to consult Dr. McLandress, the accuracy of the Horizons has steadily increased.

The Maximum Prestige Horizons of the various Areas of Identification and the individual's rating under that Horizon, though they are the pivots of the McLandress system, are only the starting point for further and vital adjustments which refine the system and establish the final order of social precedence. The principal adjustments are as follows:

(1) The Horizon Inflation Adjustment (HIA). This is the most subtle of the adjustments. An individual who is in an Area of Identification with a high MPH gains something from the very prestige of his Area — and from the reflected glory, as it were, of those with whom he is identified in the

public mind. Thus, to take an example at random, Mr. James A. Perkins, the former Vice President of the Carnegie Corporation and recently appointed President of Cornell University, has a rating of 7 as the president of a major eastern university in an area where the MPH is 8. Yet no one would suggest that Mr. Perkins' position, high though it is, is two-thirds of that of the President of the United States or quite equal to that of Senator Paul Douglas who also has a rating of 7. To correct for the effect of a high horizon, Dr. McLandress multiplies the personal rating by a figure equal to half the MPH. The President's rating of 12 is thus multiplied by one-half of the MPH for politics or by 6. This gives the President an *adjusted* score of 72. Senator Douglas (7 × 6) emerges with an adjusted score of 42. Mr. Perkins has an adjusted score of 7 × 4 or 28. It will immediately be evident that this reflects far more accurately the comparative position of the three men.

(2) The Transfer Bonus (TB). This is of the utmost importance for the McLandress system and the failure to understand and employ this adjustment explains, more than any other single factor, the failure of the pre-McLandress efforts to establish an American system of social precedence. The Bonus is also of great operative importance for any individual who wishes to move up.

As Dr. McLandress has repeatedly emphasized, prestige is multidimensional. The American system is strongly insistent on the point. A businessman, as just noted, counts for little if he is known to be *only* a businessman. But he comes quickly into his own if he is known to have penetrating views on economic development, psychiatry or modern art. The position of a lawyer who attends to his practice and takes no part in public affairs, philanthropy or civil liberties is similar. The most successful Hollywood star improves her position by having a solid competence in politics, livestock-breeding or serious literature. It is pejorative for a politician to be called "just a politician." Mr. Hoover gained greatly from having been an engineer as did Mr. Eisenhower from having been a soldier. It was important for both Mr. Truman and Mr. Kennedy that they were serious students of history. Before going into politics, Mr. Nelson Rockefeller, already a scion of established wealth and a serious philanthropist, painstakingly established a position in punditry through the Rockefeller Brothers Fund. This added measurably to his prestige as a politician. Both Mr. Gore Vidal and Mr. James Michener substantially enhanced their reputations as writers by running unsuccessfully for Congress.

The Transfer Bonus, as worked out by Dr. McLandress, is very simple. To the individual's final rating in his primary field (i.e., his rating adjusted upward by the Horizon Inflation Adjustment) is added his rating as similarly established in his secondary field plus the Bonus of one-fifth or 20 per cent. By way of illustration, Mr. Gore Vidal, just mentioned, has an adjusted rating in his primary field of letters of 16. (He has a rating of 4 in an Area with an MPH of 8 and his rating is multiplied by a Horizon Inflation Adjustment of 4.) In politics he has a score of 3 (a rating of 0.5 as a defeated candidate multiplied by half the horizon or 6). To this 3 is added an additional 20 per cent of 0.6 for a modest but respectable final rating of 19.6.

Mr. David Rockefeller, the younger brother of the Governor, is one of the most interesting examples of the exploitation of the Transfer Bonus. As President of the Chase Manhattan Bank, he has the meager score of 8 — a personal rating of 4 in an Area with an MPH of 4 multiplied by a Horizon Inflation Adjustment of 2. To this, he adds a score of 9.6 (4 × 2 + Transfer Bonus of 1.6) for established wealth. He further adds 10.8 (2 × 4.5 + 1.8) for economic punditry — it will be recalled that he once exchanged letters on economic policy with President Kennedy. Finally, he adds 7.2 for philanthropy for a total score of 35.6. Instead of a superficially modest position as a banker Mr. Rockefeller has a very strong one as a man of parts.

The Transfer Bonus, as Dr. McLandress points out, is the foundation of one of the nation's not inconsiderable industries — the public relations business. While Dr. McLandress criticizes much of the advice given by the public relations counsellor as unscientific — his own clients and patients get a much higher position for their money — he credits the public relations man who urges his clients to become active in trade expansion, juvenile delinquency, heart disease or stream pollution with having sensed, instinctively, the importance of the Transfer Bonus. During the Eisenhower administration, the many business executives who spent from a few weeks to a few months in the Department of Defense also showed, according to Dr. McLandress, a sound if often highly empirical instinct. A small investment of time brought a substantial addition to their score. The slight current use by public relations men of eccentricity and agriculture and the advice to avoid old-fashioned ostentation, all of which were once much favored by men of wealth, also reflect the scientific reality.

Two final adjustments are made by McLandress. A man who is evidently on the way up gets an appropriate percentage added to his total score. This reflects the special American appreciation of the man who is moving ahead or on the make. A man who is on the way down gets an equivalent but somewhat heavier deduction. Our system of social precedence is notably hard on the falling star.

As a related matter, the individual who retires, is defeated or is otherwise removed from his Area of Identification — the ex-Senator, ex-tycoon, ex-bank president, former actress, onetime glamour girl — immediately has his or her score divided by a factor of ten. (For an ex-President of the United States, the factor is only three. Alone among retired Americans, they retain a relatively high position.) According to Dr. McLandress, the precipitate decline in score when an individual gives up office also has important social consequences. Men who are still in office are acutely conscious of the fate of the lions of yesteryear — of the Homer Capeharts, Homer Fergusons, Neil McElroys, William Knowlands, Clarence Randalls, Mark Clarks, Richard Nixons, and Douglas MacArthurs. As a result, resistance to retirement has become one of the fierce, primal instincts of modern man. Dr. McLandress notes that at the top levels of other societies such as Germany and France, it is equally strong.

Last of all, Dr. McLandress allows for one quite different source of social precedence. This is the old and exceedingly well-tried technique of seeking position not by building up one's own score but by association with someone who has a satisfactory score. The McLandress calculations show that an individual can ordinarily count on having approximately ten per cent of the score of a person with whom he is associated as a personal assistant, a known and intimate golfing companion, fishing companion, fellow raconteur, favorite bridge partner, regular social guest or associate from boyhood. This is not high but for many people who seek position, it is not only the best but the only available technique of advancement.[2]

[2] For a wife Association Prestige, to use Dr. McLandress' term, is of course higher and may, on occasion, approach that of the principal. For clandestine associates, it may be lower.

Association Prestige, in Dr. McLandress' view, also usefully explains familiar social behavior. The speech writer or legman who labors to advance the presidential ambitions of a governor or senator is commonly considered a model of selflessness and is so described by both journalists and historians. According to Dr. McLandress, he may be engaged, in fact, on a well-considered program for raising his own rating. Even the secretary or stenographer who attaches herself to a rising young executive, publisher or pundit may be stimulated less by Freudian involvement than by old-fashioned ambition.

Association Prestige also clarifies the old problem of the ambitious and discriminating hostess. She is not, as many have imagined, serving idle vanity or seeking political or cultural influence. She is far more likely to be engaged in a well-calculated effort to advance in the American peerage. Thus, a New York hostess whose house, in the course of time, comes to be identified in discriminating circles with (say) Adlai Stevenson, Roger Stevens, Marietta Tree, Grayson Kirk, and Lucius Clay accumulates for herself a very respectable score.

The foregoing places the McLandress system in the public domain. (The full scores for a group of representative Americans are given in the accompanying table.) The consequences of the full disclosure of the system are certain to be considerable. Dr. McLandress has himself suggested that one effect will be to stabilize the Maximum Prestige Horizons except possibly those such as Hollywood, athletics and banking which, being already in decline, may be subject to even more adverse effects. As long as the MPH's were subjective, the

	John F. Kennedy	Nelson Rockefeller	George Romney	Marlon Brando
Primary Area of Identification	Politics	Politics	Politics	Theater (Hollywood)
MPH	12	12	12	9
Personal Rating	12	8	6	9
Horizon Inflation Adjustment	×6	×6	×6	×4.5
Adjusted Rating	72	48	36	40.5
Secondary Area	History	Wealth (Established)	Business	
MPH	6	4	5	
Personal Rating	3	4	4	
Horizon Inflation Adjustment	×3	×2	×2.5	
Adjusted Secondary Rating	9	8	10	
Transfer Bonus (+20%)	1.8	1.6	2	
Cumulative Rating	82.8	57.6	48	40.5
Tertiary and Further Areas	Wealth (Established)	Philanthropy Punditry		
Total of Tertiary and Further Ratings	7.2	9		
Cumulative Rating	90.0	66.6	48	40.5
Dynamic Adjustment		−5%	10%	−14%
Amount		−3.3	4.8	−5.7
Cumulative Rating	90.0	63.3	52.8	34.8
Ex Factor (if applicable)				
Final Rating	90.0	63.3	52.8	34.8

A rating based on Association Prestige, i.e. close association with one of the above, is derived simply by dividing the particular celebrity's score by ten. Thus, an intimate of Nelson Rockefeller has a rating of 6.33; of Norman Cousins, 1.43; and of Norman Mailer, 1.08.

Paul Dudley White	Norman Cousins	Walter Cronkite	Monroe Jackson Rathbone	Norman Mailer	Harold Stassen
Medicine	Publishing	Theater (TV)	Business	Letters	Politics
6 6 ×3 18	7 3 ×3.5 10.5	8 4 ×4 16	5 4.5 ×2.5 11.25	7 3.5 ×3.5 12.25	12 6 ×6 36
Athletics	Punditry			Eccentricity	Education (University)
6 2 ×3 6 1.2 25.2	9 1 ×4.5 4.5 .9 15.9	16	11.25	1 .5 × .5 .25 .05 12.55	0* 0 0 0 0 36
25.2	15.9	16	11.25	12.55	36
25.2	−10% −1.6 14.3	−12% −1.9 14.1	11.25	−14% −1.8 10.8	36
					÷10
25.2	14.3	14.1	11.25	10.8	3.6

* Although Mr. Stassen became President of the University of Pennsylvania after leaving his governorship, no added score or Transfer Bonus is given to a onetime politician, military figure or public servant who goes into education or business. Necessity, not versatility, is assumed to govern the acceptance of these positions.

prestige associated with various Areas was subject to subtle re-evaluation and change. Now people will tend to anchor their assessment to the McLandress findings.

The other effects are reasonably predictable from the use to which the ratings have already been put by McLandress' clients. Any sensitive and self-conscious person will henceforth not only compute his rating but keep it up to date. This is insured by the fact that the mathematics are within the competence of the person of average education and the individual running into difficulty can, in any case, resort to the nearest high school mathematics teacher.

Public relations men will henceforth have their services on a far more scientific basis. Political and other careers will be more systematically planned. Leading Washington and New York hostesses have long been clients of Dr. McLandress and have planned their social activities around his ratings. Now this practice will spread to other centers and the competition for highly rated guests is certain to increase. It is not beyond the bounds of possibility that Washington papers will one day print total and average scores for important dinners and other major social occasions. A service which will supply the current rating of any individual, as similar services now supply credit ratings, will almost certainly be launched in the next year or two. It has also been suggested that an individual's current rating might be stamped on his credit card. This would insure that hotels, airlines, florist shops, night clubs and restaurants would automatically accord the individual the consideration to which he is entitled.

However, the greatest benefits of the aristocratic ready reckoner, as some McLandress clients have dubbed the system, are probably greatest in the realm of the psyche. "Subjectivity," Dr. McLandress has said, "is the enemy of contentment." It has meant that the individual did not know where he stood, where he was going, or what he could intelligently do to alter an unsatisfactory position. With social precedence a matter of objective calculation, exact knowledge and solid effort replace aimless worry. Confidence is enormously enhanced. Indeed among really successful Americans, few now don their dinner clothes or start for their cars without saying a silent word of thanks for the work of Dr. Herschel McLandress.

The Fully Automated Foreign Policy

"This innovation in communications technique represents an important contribution to management effectiveness and will aid us in the achievement of our foreign policy objectives."
—Statement by Dean Rusk, Secretary of State, inaugurating the Automatic Data Exchange (ADX) developed by the International Telephone and Telegraph Corporation, as reported in the New York Herald Tribune, September 19, 1962.

THE BIG rectangular room was quiet, oppressively quiet. The Secretary drummed his fingers on the desk and let his eyes travel over the chairs, sofas, mahogany plywood paneling, the framed commission from the President of the United States. Once more he thought how the decorator had managed to make it hideous without looking expensive. He rose from his chair and looked down at the pickets making their endless rounds in the street below. His eye caught the gleam of the Potomac and the distant line of the Pentagon. He returned to his chair and rang for his secretary. Faintly, even through the soundproofed walls, he heard the buzz. When she came in, he said, "I suppose you notice it too?"

"It's very lonely but I think I'm getting accustomed."

A little awkwardly, conscious of the unnatural gesture, he reached over and patted her hand. "I think we both will. When does Dr. McLandress get here?"

"He should have come by now. He wanted to get an early plane to Boston. Oh, here he is."

The door of the office framed a large, broad-shouldered man of around fifty in a well-cut suit of dark worsted. He gave the impression of dressing with taste but no particular care. Above the high cheekbones and deep angular lines of his face, his high bald head stood in sharp contrast with the heavy gray eyebrows. The Secretary rose to greet his visitor.

"Well, so from today I'm on my own?"

"Not exactly. You have an installation which will do everything your boys ever did and much faster."

"I know. It still seems so . . . impersonal."

"Let's run through the day. That's your best reassurance."

"All right," said the Secretary, "only I wish it hadn't left me with this big building. Sometimes it gives me the creeps."

As they started toward the door, the Secretary glanced down again at the picket line. A little cluster had gathered around

Professor Rostow who was gesticulating vehemently. He noticed Averell Harriman, tall, handsome, patrician, leaning over to listen, and beside him the short, compact figure of Ambassador and former Under Secretary George McGhee. Behind, also attentive as though waiting to speak, was Ambassador Chester Bowles. At a little distance, one of the policemen stood eying the group. Marching stolidly under their signs were Under Secretary Ball, U. Alexis Johnson, Mennen Williams, the former Ambassador to the Court of St. James's, David Bruce — others. There was scarcely a man he did not recognize on sight.

"I wonder what Walt was saying," the Secretary mused as he followed Dr. McLandress into the big empty anteroom. "There must be some things that a machine can't . . ." He suppressed the rest of the thought.

Moments later, under the eye of the great psychometricist, he was twirling the combination of a heavy steel door. It swung open, and the two men stepped inside. The Secretary looked at the neutral gray steel cabinets, the green and white console, the occasional flashing red buttons of light, the racks of coded punch cards, the highspeed printer, the rolls of printed tape. His mind started back again, this time to the morning staff meeting when each man in turn had told of the troubles in his part of the world and the policies under discussion. Again he suppressed a twinge of nostalgia. "What do we have first?" he asked.

"Nothing on Afghanistan or Albania," Dr. McLandress said. "'Argentina, routine seizure of government by tank detachment. Free elections promised.' The first important thing in the alphabetic file is Berlin. Code Be. 1.046. 'Khrush-

chev in Sofia threatens to sign a peace treaty with East Germany.' "

"What is our reply?"

" 'We stand willing to negotiate but we cannot act under threat or pressure and we must not make concessions. The reunification of Germany is essential but we do not thereby concede the existence of East Germany. We support the brave people of West Berlin.' Teletyped all posts. Released AP, UPI, all local Bureaus. Every hour on VOA. Fulbright to be informed at proper time."

"That's certainly according to policy," said the Secretary. "I'm glad that one wasn't in the 'o' series. Lyndon Johnson again. Or Clay? Good God. What's next?"

"This one is 'o.' Brazil. Code Br. 0.464. 'Immediate threat of bankruptcy and economic collapse. $75,000,000.' "

"I'll call the Secretary of the Treasury."

"It now goes automatically, Mr. Secretary," McLandress said gently.

"Anything from China?"

"Yes. Ch. 2.00. 'Threat to invade mainland. Demand for American support.' "

"Same answer?"

"Yes, almost. 'We are firmly committed to the liberation of the Chinese people. Our policy of unleashment remains unchanged. However, the time may not yet be imminent . . .' "

The men worked on through the tapes. At France, there was a crisis in the upper "o" series, a speech in Toulouse by General de Gaulle demanding that the United States give up its independent nuclear deterrent, confine its foreign policy to Cuba. American withdrawal from NATO requested. The

Secretary tucked in his pocket a copy of the press release that had already gone out: "As between friends and partners, honest differences of opinion are occasionally inevitable. However, the nations of the North Atlantic Community have never been more united or stronger in their determination . . ."

Many of the items were routine. At Iraq (Code Ir. 1.24.) came word of a coup. Seventy-six army officers executed on television. "The situation remains unclear. The Department is keeping in closest touch."

At the United States (Code U.S. 4.25.) was a speech by Dean Acheson. "Mr. Acheson was speaking only in his personal capacity as a member of the law firm of Covington and Burling and former Assistant Secretary of the Treasury."

The two men continued steadily and finally, a little after noon, Dr. McLandress handed the Secretary Yu. 10.050., an administrative message from Belgrade: "EMB AUTOMATION NOW COMPLETE. TAKING LEAVE TONIGHT. KENNAN."

Below was the answer: "CONGRATULATIONS. BEST OF LUCK WITH YOUR LECTURES."

The Secretary glanced through the White House tapes. The British Prime Minister would arrive on Thursday on his fortnightly visit. It was the one concession he would not make to automation. The President would be urged to use the occasion to press for the merger of BBC with French television, "a further stride in forging the unity of the nations of the free world." The gold outflow had diminished although copper and zinc were still going in some quantity. The Secretary leafed through a speech which had been prepared for delivery at a meeting of the Foreign Service Institute, copies of which were neatly stacked by the printer.

> Most of all, we seek prompt decisions . . . timely action to-day may forestall grave crises tomorrow . . . press the search for new initiatives . . . break with routine . . . originality . . .

The speech had come from the machine as scheduled the day before, a harmless error in programming, Dr. McLandress had explained. The Secretary dropped the copy in the wastepaper basket. The morning's work was over.

The two men shook hands at the elevator. The Secretary looked again at his watch and thought of escaping to a companionable lunch at the Metropolitan Club. But he knew that the pickets would by now be stacking their signs outside the entrance and trooping in for a martini and discussion of the day's foreign policy developments. He could not face them. He pressed the Up button, got off at the top floor and went along the hall to the Secretary's dining room. Dropping two quarters into the slot, he took out a plate of corned beef hash and then went to the dispenser for a glass of milk. Glancing out of the window, he noticed that one lone picket was keeping guard — he recognized the slightly stooped shoulders of Ambassador Charles Bohlen and his eye took in the meticulous wording of the sign. He wondered for a moment why he hadn't invited his secretary to join him. She would be eating alone in the cafeteria. Then he sat down at a table and was lost in thought.

"Some inventions," Dr. Herschel McLandress has written, "such as the sewing machine and the steam engine are like

Athena in their origin. They spring full-blown from the head of the inventor; no one could predict their arrival or say why they arrived at a particular moment. But there are others — the automatic gearshift, the supersonic airplane, color television — which are predestined and predictable. Like a piece of coal on a conveyor belt, anyone could look and see them on the way. The automation of American foreign policy was of this sort. Few innovations were ever more predictable." [1]

The long-range cause of the automation of American foreign policy, in the view of Dr. McLandress, was automation in other industries. As labor was released by the automobile industry, the steel industry, by modern large-scale agriculture, it was increasingly absorbed into the administration of the armed forces and the making of foreign policy. There was nothing subtle about this. After earlier wars, officers, NCO's and enlisted men had bade farewell to their units and headed for a homestead, a job as a factory foreman or a place at the bench. Following World War II and the Korean War, these opportunities no longer existed. So men got a job in the Pentagon or went to the State Department. A generation ago, the boy from a farm in rural Michigan set off for Detroit and a job at Ford. As automation closed this door, he prepared himself for a life in diplomacy.

Throughout the country in the years following World War II, enlightened programs for the training of men for foreign policy were launched by the universities. If these programs were to succeed, there had to be employment for the people so trained. Congress and the Executive moved readily, far

[1] Herschel McLandress. "The Automation of American Foreign Policy: A Retrospective View." *Foreign Affairs,* XCVII.

more readily than is commonly supposed, to provide the jobs.[2]

The immediate cause of foreign policy automation, in Dr. McLandress' view, was the spread among foreign policy administrators in the years after World War II of what, with a gift for homely illustration, he calls "the potato syllogism." As a potato farmer faces more complex and difficult harvesting conditions — a heavy crop, wet soil, imminent frost, an increasingly infirm market prospect — he adds to his harvesting crew. Following this simple pattern, as the problems of foreign policy became increasingly intricate, urgent and baffling after World War II, those in charge increased proportionately the number of men to handle them. Some of the problems being infinitely difficult, the possibility was not remote that the number working on them would be infinitely large.[3]

[2] The factors influencing the level of employment in the public services have only recently been clarified by a lengthy research project conducted by the Bureau of the Budget. This has culminated in what has come to be called The Dawes-Bell Law. The DBL, as it is known to public administrators and to which Dr. McLandress attaches high significance, states that whereas in many branches of economic activity employment depends on the number of job openings available, in the public service, as also in the advertising business, social science investigation and university administration, the level of employment regularly depends on the number of men available and devoting their time to the creation of job opportunities.

Thus, in the field of foreign policy, which is strongly subject to the DBL, the availability of a group of North Central Asian specialists will lead to speeches, panel discussions, monographs on foreign policy, thoughtful articles in *The New York Times Magazine,* lectures at the National War College and Congressional testimony all stressing the importance and complexity of North Central Asian problems and the urgent need for strengthening research, intelligence, diplomatic representation and administrative and logistic support in the NCA field. This discussion will continue until action taken in response thereto results in the employment of the available NCA specialists and the articles thus cease to be written.

[3] Elsewhere Dr. McLandress notes that in 1940 the number of employees of the Department of State was 6,302; in 1946 it was 21,966; by 1962 it was 40,216.

"In fact, the parallel between potato harvesting and the making of foreign policy is not exact. To increase the number of men working on a foreign policy problem — Berlin, Castro, Viet Nam — is to increase the number of men whose agreement must be obtained before action is taken. The more men whose agreement must be obtained, the more time required.

"If the number at work on a given job is large enough, action, it would seem to follow, will be indefinitely postponed. Although this tendency does exist, things work out somewhat differently in practice. In many foreign policy situations, action is often unavoidable. Accordingly, while no new step can command agreement, something must still be done. So opinion will eventually coalesce on whatever has been done before. Those who aspire to a position of leadership will realize this and urge the existing or previous action. Others will fall in behind and so confirm the position of leadership of those who urge the status quo. Even a large group of men can reach agreement provided it is on positions previously taken." [4]

There were many who suggested to Dr. McLandress that, in its effect on American foreign policy, the potato syllogism was not adverse. They noted that the truly sophisticated man argues not for the wisdom or even the prudence of a foreign policy but for its continuity. Few things more clearly mark the amateur in diplomacy than his inability to see that even the change from the wrong policy to the right policy involves the admission of previous error and hence is damaging to national prestige. As a built-in source of continuity, the potato syllogism was held to be admirable rather than otherwise.

[4] "The Automation of American Foreign Policy," op. cit.

Working on Dr. McLandress' side, however, were the very great delays inherent in the old system. All opinions, all research, all intelligence had necessarily to be heard, evaluated and then considered. Given the large number of policymakers produced by the potato syllogism, there would always be a number expressing themselves in favor of some change, however slight. Accordingly, even a simple affirmation of the existing policy might take weeks or even months. In a fast-moving world, this eventually became intolerable. In the spring of 1962, it became known that the American Ambassador to the USSR had to request Mr. Khrushchev to delay for several weeks a routine attack on the nuclear tests on Christmas Island because agreement had not been reached on repeating the previous replies to his last denunciation. The Policy Planning Staff of the State Department then produced its fateful paper entitled, "Continuity in Foreign Policy as Modified by Discontinuity along the Time Parameter."

In recommending that Dr. McLandress be called in for study and to make recommendations for "an effective acceleration of the necessarily multivariate character of a sound decision-making process," there had been no thought that any action would result. As Dr. McLandress himself has said, "It is a well understood principle in the administration of American foreign policy that study and recommendation do not lead to revision of policy. Rather, the continuity of American policy is partly protected by the practice of ordering a study when anyone proposes change."

But Dr. McLandress' recommendations *were* accepted. No one could make a dent in the logic of this quiet but unexpectedly forceful man. "The formulation of foreign policy is the reiteration of the previous position. That reiteration is now compromised by time-consuming discussion. So long as you have people, you will have discussion. But to get the previous decision, you do not need people. You need only to classify and code the various crises and program them into a computer along with the established response. For the given crisis, the machine will then produce the right response and do it instantaneously. BUT YOU MUST ELIMINATE THE PEOPLE."

On the last point, Dr. McLandress was uncompromising, obdurate, ruthless. As noted, logic was on his side. So were the men from IBM. So were many members of Congress who saw an arrangement which would insure continuity in the nation's Cuban policy. The potato syllogism prevented the policymakers from reacting. Meetings were still in progress on the day that the machine ground out the rectangular cards with the cropped corner, the cabalistic holes and the neat message:

THE DEPARTMENT OF STATE THANKS YOU FOR YOUR ——— YEARS AND ——— MONTHS OF DEVOTED AND LOYAL SERVICE AND WISHES YOU A REWARDING RETIREMENT. UNDER AMENDED RETIREMENT REGULATIONS, YOUR PENSION WILL BE $00,000.00 PER ANNUM. THANK YOU AGAIN.

McLandress had triumphed. The decision to engage in peaceful picketing at the token level was taken by officers as individuals.

The Secretary was surprised to see that it was nearly half past two. He wondered if he had dozed off. Back in his office, he sent his secretary for the latest tapes of the day's business and then experienced the slightly annoying sense of uneasiness which he always felt when the white phone rang. It was only a White House secretary asking if he could run through the day's business at 6:20. The Secretary noted that he had something over three hours ahead of him and took up the tapes.

At four-thirty, a semi-literate ambassador from a minor Latin American republic came in. The man was congenitally incapable of understanding the notes and demarches which came into his Embassy on the teletype. The Secretary read him a protest in basic English against a decree making membership in opposition parties subject to a life sentence and reflected that the fellow probably didn't have any trouble deciphering a bank draft. A call came in from Stevenson in New York. His Security Council speech had come from the computer with an unpunctuated paragraph. They chatted companionably for twenty minutes and the Secretary authorized the Ambassador to exercise discretion. He wondered, for a moment, if McLandress would have approved. At six, his secretary brought in the afternoon tapes and he finished reading them in his car.

Things still went well.

Albania. Code Al. 4.44. "Diplomatic relations severed by both China and the Soviet Union. Asking recognition by West."

"No action. Await real evidence of abandonment of aggressive intentions, acceptance of United Nations Charter and willingness to take wheat under Public Law 480."

Ecuador. Code Ec. 0.45. "Impending bankruptcy."

"$10,000,000."

In Germany, there was a crisis in the upper "o" series. Code

Ge. 0.898. Speech in Dinkelsbuhl by Chancellor. "The United States must sever relations with Soviet Union and Rumania. Stop honoring East German postage stamps. Announcement of West German loan of DM 600,000,000 for financing necessary trade with East Germany."

"As between friends and partners, honest differences of opinion are occasionally inevitable. However, the nations of the North Atlantic Community have never . . ."

Geneva. Code UNrm 4.55. Speech by Soviet delegate calling for general and complete disarmament.

"The United States stands committed to the principle of complete and general disarmament. It will not compromise the safety of the free world."

Persepolis. Code Pe. 0.457. (Delayed.) "Reported land fighting with small Greek forces. Naval reverse at Salamis."

"The Department is keeping in closest touch. The situation remains unclear."

India. Code In. 10.05. "Internal. Embassy asking clarification of instructions."

"Sympathize your problem. However, do not feel at this juncture any departure from existing policy necessary or desirable."

On several of the crises, the tapes showed no response. Dr. McLandress had explained the need to avoid breaking too radically with established tradition.

The car pulled up at the West Basement of the White House and the Secretary nodded familiarly to the Secret Service man as he passed inside the door. As he climbed the stairs, he was struck by the warm and pleasant hum of offices that were filled with people. He went along the narrow corridor to the President's office.

The President was running through the tapes that had just come from the White House printer. "Glad to see you," he said briefly and motioned the Secretary to a chair. In a minute, he was finished.

"Do you really think this machine can handle every situation — everything?"

"I think so, Mr. President. You remember that home economist in Saigon last week. Caught doing the Twist in her shower?"

"That was pretty impressive. But what about always basing our policy on what was done before? Aren't we ever moving forward?"

"You know, Mr. President. You once asked for some new policies yourself."

"Good God. The delay that caused. But one thing . . ."

"Yes, Mr. President."

The Secretary noticed for the first time that the President was holding one of the rectangular cards with the cropped corner.

The Secretary left his car and driver at the basement entrance and walked out on Pennsylvania Avenue. Three pickets were strolling back and forth in front of the White House. The Secret Service men watched from their box. The Secretary walked over to the Honorable W. Walton Butterworth and, with something akin to a feeling of pleasure, relieved him of his sign.

The Confidence Machine

"The confidence of the business world has been gravely impaired."
—*U.S. News and World Report*. Also: *Wall Street Journal*, *Indianapolis Star*, *Los Angeles Times* and *Standard and Poor's*.

A FEW weeks ago the Secretary of Commerce rose from his desk in his impressive office in the Commerce Department in Washington, D.C., and joined his Under Secretary, two Assistant Secretaries and a group of other aides in the anteroom. Without haste, with firm, rather measured steps they moved in a small procession through the halls and down the corridors of the Commerce Building to the office of the Commissioner of Patents. Here they were joined by the Secretary of the Treasury, the Chairman of the Board of Governors of the

Federal Reserve System, the Chairman of the Council of Economic Advisers, the President's Science Adviser and the head of the National Science Foundation. Present also were two scholarly-looking men whom the Secretary greeted with special warmth. The little group then watched the formal filing of Patent Application No. 3,007,632. After a short speech and more handshaking, the Secretary returned to his office and picked up the white phone. When a familiar voice came over the wire, the Secretary said: "I have the pleasure of telling you, sir, that the patent application has been filed."

Back came the reply: "Mr. Secretary, that is great! Great!"

The subject of the small ceremony and this cryptic conversation was a small rectangular box of light beige-colored plastic, measuring about four by six inches and about three-quarters of an inch thick, that hangs suspended on a loop of black ribbon about twelve inches long. On the top is a recessed dial; the back is perforated. It resembles a small, very thin transistor radio and the resemblance is not entirely accidental.

The formal name of the device is The Sonic Subliminal Support Apparatus, Mark II. No such title is susceptible to everyday use and scientists have already nicknamed it the Confidence Machine.

The Confidence Machine is the product of the fruitful collaboration of two of America's most original minds, Dr. Herschel McLandress, the famous Boston psychometricist, and Professor Edward Detweiller, formerly of the Massachusetts Institute of Technology and senior partner of Plympton Associates, the firm of advanced electronic engineers of

Lincoln, Massachusetts. Dr. McLandress and Professor Detweiller were the two scientists who were present to be congratulated by the Secretary on the day of the patent filing. That evening they were guests of honor at a black-tie dinner and chamber-music recital at the White House.

The history of the Confidence Machine dates from the very first weeks of the present Administration in 1961. Then perceptive and historically minded aides of the new President, of whom there were so many, gathered to discuss a problem which has plagued Presidents since the days of Franklin D. Roosevelt: how to retain the confidence of the important business executives of the country and restore confidence, should it be lost. They were determined that if President Kennedy faced the problem there would be an answer on tap.

These men knew that business confidence was a fragile thing. They also knew that there were conflicting theories as to the factors on which it depended. Wisely deciding to get professional help, they turned naturally to Dr. Herschel McLandress whose work was well known especially to the Harvard and M.I.T. members of the new President's staff. They knew that, perhaps uniquely among Americans, Dr. McLandress could bring the trained insights of psychology, psychiatry, and psychometrics to bear on the problem of business confidence. He readily agreed to undertake the job.

Dr. McLandress' first task was to clear away the misconceptions surrounding the subject and to tie down, once and for all, the propositions that are fully susceptible to scientific proof. This he did in what he calls "the five fundamental theorems of business confidence." In somewhat abbreviated form, they are:

(1) The confidence of the business executive in a President is inversely related to the state of business.

In laymen's language, this means that confidence will always be high when business is poor and low when business is good. According to Dr. McLandress, the proposition holds without limit, which is to say that the worse business is, the higher business confidence will be, and the better business is, the more confidence will suffer.

In support of this theorem, which some economists have dubbed the McLandress paradox, Dr. McLandress notes that, among modern Presidents, none enjoyed so completely the confidence of the important men of business as Mr. Hoover. Under no President was business so bad. In the early days of the Roosevelt administration, business was still very poor. Mr. Roosevelt, in those days while the Depression was still very severe, enjoyed a very considerable measure of business confidence. As business revived in the later years of his Administration, he lost the confidence of leading businessmen. With the peaks of business activity during the war years, confidence in Roosevelt reached a very low level.

Under President Truman business conditions continued very good and hence confidence remained low. With President Eisenhower came a recurrence of minor recessions and a slower rate of economic growth. As a result, the confidence of business executives revived. However, business under Eisenhower was much better than under Hoover and hence Eisenhower never enjoyed the complete confidence that was accorded his predecessor. One considerable group in the business community continued to regard him with grave misgivings.

When President Kennedy came to office, business was in a minor state of recession. Accordingly, the initial reaction to Kennedy was one of considerable confidence. In 1961 and subsequently as recovery proceeded, confidence in Mr. Kennedy inevitably declined. This evidence is considered definitive by scientists and it has even impressed a number of fair-minded businessmen. "A far better correlation than that relating lung cancer to cigarette smoking," a leading tobacco executive recently conceded.

(2) Government action and inaction both gravely impair business confidence.

In support of this proposition, Dr. McLandress notes that business executives react unfavorably to an upward spiral of prices and wages and a declining value of the dollar. This is inflation. If allowed to go unchecked, it leads to seriously impaired morale. Business executives also react unfavorably to government efforts to stabilize prices and wages and thus arrest inflation. This is wage- and price-fixing and highly inconsistent with American traditions.

(3) Reassurance of business by a President has an unfavorable effect on confidence.

In 1930 and 1931 Mr. Hoover made statements designed to reassure business executives. This was the only time in his long career that he did not enjoy the complete confidence of men of standing in the business community. President Kennedy, like President Roosevelt before him, has tried to calm fear and make clear his friendly intentions toward business.

These statements have had a sharply adverse effect on confidence.

Dr. McLandress explains this by what he calls the *Inverse Insecurity Factor.* "A business executive who observes a President trying to reassure him naturally wonders why. And naturally he concludes that the President is hostile, otherwise why would he think reassurance necessary. Reflecting on this, he naturally loses confidence."

(4) Unkind words do not enhance business confidence.

If reassuring words diminish confidence, it is natural to suppose that robust, muscular or critical language might restore it. Both President Roosevelt and President Kennedy have tested this hypothesis. The effect on business confidence has again been adverse. "To refer to a business executive as a 'money changer' to be driven from the temple as did Mr. Roosevelt or to identify him with canine ancestry as has Mr. Kennedy clearly breeds a measure of resentment," Dr. McLandress observes. "This impairs confidence."

(5) That politics has a bearing on business confidence is unproven.

Journalists and other commentators have argued that businessmen, being Republicans, had confidence in Presidents Hoover and Eisenhower because *they* were Republicans. Such facile and unscientific conclusions drive Dr. McLandress almost to anger. One can as reasonably assume, he says, that businessmen are Republican *because* of the confidence inspired by these Republican Presidents. Who can say what is cause and what is effect. "Politics and science, like oil and water, are incompatible."

*

"The conclusion to be drawn from these principles," Dr. McLandress noted in his first memorandum to the informal White House staff committee, "is crystal clear. Business confidence is not determined by what a President says or by what he does, and any action he takes, if it affects confidence at all, will affect it adversely.[1] On the contrary, as anyone sensitive to the lessons of modern psychology and psychiatry would suspect, the problem of business confidence impinges on deeper factors of personality. More specifically, the modern business executive is like every other human being. He must have some figure to whom he can turn mentally for reassurance and support in moments of insecurity and doubt—someone who serves the function, as it is known to the psychologist, of a Sustaining Presence. Given his position and responsibilities and his relation to the economic life of the nation, it is the President of the United States to whom the business executive turns almost instinctively. It is a matter purely of the President's personality whether he provides the needed reassurance or whether he does not."

Among the Presidents who had the capacity to provide this reassurance in high degree, Dr. McLandress mentions Mr. Hoover and Mr. Eisenhower. Neither of the Roosevelts had this quality. Nor did Mr. Truman. It is now reasonably evident that President Kennedy is not a Sustaining Presence for the average business executive.

[1] There is one theoretical line of action favorable to confidence which is consistent with these principles and that would be to promote a business depression since confidence is always high in bad times. However, as Dr. McLandress notes, this would be a remedy with unfortunate side effects, and it is also a line of policy on which economists have done no work. Dr. McLandress does observe that we have here the explanation as to why business executives always react unfavorably to the economic advisers of a President. These latter will always be seeking to improve business conditions, a course of action which, on the record, can only impair confidence.

In science, as in medicine, an accurate diagnosis, however discouraging, is often the first step toward a remedy. And it was from the seemingly discouraging conclusion on the relation of confidence to personality that the McLandress solution emerged. For almost immediately the thought occurred to Dr. McLandress that if the Presidential personality were inadequate as a Sustaining Presence, perhaps a substitute support could somehow be inserted into the executive's life. If the President did not serve, might not the executive be given the psychological equivalent, as it were, of an artificial limb? More specifically, might not those who had once served as a Sustaining Presence be reintroduced in the executive's life as continuing psychological support?

Pursuing this hypothesis, Dr. McLandress invited to his clinic a group of New England business executives, all of whom were known to be suffering from severely shaken confidence. He asked them to spend several hours listening to speeches of Herbert Hoover and to speeches and selected press conferences of Dwight D. Eisenhower. They were then subject to careful psychological tests. Over half of the executives showed a positive response. A minority emerged from the experiment exuding confidence.

This confidence evaporated in the course of a few days and more rapidly if, in the interim, the executive were exposed to any strong reminder of the Administration. A Presence could be devised. But if the effect were to be durable and useful, some way had to be found to keep this re-created Presence constantly with the executive. It was at this juncture that Dr. McLandress called in Professor Detweiller.

He asked his old friend if he could design a small apparatus, capable of being worn by a subject under his clothing, which would play recorded speeches or statements for as much as twenty-four hours a day. Professor Detweiller, in turn, called in his assistants and set to work. The result was The Sonic Support Apparatus.[2] A number of members of the executive group who had responded to Hoover and Eisenhower were persuaded to try out the device. When it was operated for several hours a day, their confidence was completely sustained.

However, problems remained. The sound of a voice, however muted, coming from the vicinity of the executive's chestbone invited questions and a measure of jocular comment. As a result, one or two executives, more self-conscious than

[2] The first model — the Mark I — was bulky and could not be worn under a dress shirt or with any comfort under night garments. A fully transistorized and miniaturized version — Mark II — lies comfortably and unobtrusively against the chest so that its presence cannot be detected from the outside.

the rest, rejected the machine and it was obvious that others would do likewise. More serious, nearly half of the executives in the sample did not respond to the sonic presence of either Hoover or Eisenhower.

The problem of second-person audibility, as it was called, proved to have a simple solution. Having in mind that few of the executives ever listened carefully to the speeches or press conferences of Hoover or Eisenhower in real life, Dr. McLandress decided that words might well have their restorative effect in being uttered and not in being registered on the ear. Accordingly, he had the executives test their responses in progressively lower ranges of audibility. He found that they remained responsive down to a faint hum providing that the time of application was proportionately extended. At these subliminal sonic levels, the required applications for members of the sample ranged from sixteen to twenty-two hours a day.[3,4,5]

The problem of the nonresponding executive was less easily solved. There was a clue, however, in the fact that some executives responded only to Mr. Hoover, some only to Mr. Eisenhower. Perhaps there might be other Sustaining Pres-

[3] In a period of exceptional activity by the President or members of his family, the required application had to be somewhat higher.

[4] One of the experimental subjects, not an executive but a retired faculty member of the Harvard Graduate School of Business Administration, required an aggregate of twenty-three-and-a-half hours of the speeches of Mr. Hoover. On occasion there was some residual impairment even after a full twenty-four-hour application.

[5] Confidence was considered restored if the subject was brought within a range of 95-105 per cent of full confidence. In many instances, longer applications brought a subject to 115 or 120 per cent, leaving an excess of confidence of up to 15 or 20 per cent. In Dr. McLandress' view, the exuding of confidence, at least above a certain safety margin, serves no useful purpose.

ences; perhaps, indeed, a President might be the surrogate for a more fundamental Presence which, if discovered, would serve even more satisfactorily. This hypothesis proved fruitful. Enlarging the original test group to make it representative of the country as a whole, Dr. McLandress found that two executives who were negative to Hoover and Eisenhower responded to readings from the autobiography and of selected aphorisms of Calvin Coolidge, including his well-known remark that "The business of America is business." A Cincinnati executive responded similarly to readings from the speeches of William McKinley and an elderly Upstate New Yorker to the inaugural address of Chester A. Arthur.

But the fundamental or nonpresidential Presences turned out to be far more important although they were discovered only by a tedious process of trial and error. Jeremy Bentham (readings from *Manual of Political Economy* and *Defence of Usury*) was discovered at an early stage to be the Sustaining Presence of four members of the enlarged group, including one head of an automobile finance corporation, one vice-president of a chain of small loan companies, and two investment bankers. By contrast, Herbert Spencer was not found to be a Sustaining Presence until, after lengthy experiments with readings from *Social Statics*, it occurred to Dr. McLandress one afternoon to substitute *The Principles of Biology*. Six members of the group, all suffering substantial impairment, responded to Spencer's discussion of the survival of the fittest. Readings from Adam Smith's *Wealth of Nations* were not only worthless but had such an adverse effect on two executives of the electrical industry that Dr. McLandress deemed it wise to remove Smith's work from the experiment.

Two executives of the test group responded to the epigrams of Commodore Vanderbilt and two to readings from the biography by Allan Nevins of the elder Rockefeller. An airlines executive and the owner of a New York newspaper, both emerging from a round of labor troubles, were found to respond well to simple repetition of the brief comment on labor relations of the late George F. Baer.[6]

For three members of the test group, the Sustaining Presence was the late Senator Robert A. Taft and one Midwestern executive responded, somewhat surprisingly, to the speeches (as a vice-presidential candidate) of John W. Bricker. The

[6] Mr. Baer affirmed in 1903 the view that "The rights and interests of the laboring man will be protected and cared for, not by labor agitators, but by the Christian men to whom God in His infinite wisdom has given control of the property interests of the country."

Sustaining Presence of one Texas entrepreneur was Joseph R. McCarthy. A scholarly executive in Des Moines was sustained by readings from Alexander Hamilton's reports on the public credit and on manufactures. No businessman was sustained by Adlai Stevenson, Earl Warren, Thomas E. Dewey, Leon Keyserling, Lyndon Johnson, Alfred M. Landon, Paul Douglas, Gaylord Nelson, Kenneth Keating, Endicott Peabody, Sherman Adams, Walter Reuther, George Romney, Clifford Case, Edwin A. Walker or Mr. or Mrs. Paul Hoffman. This, Dr. McLandress cites as further evidence that there is no relation between politics and a role as a Sustaining Presence.

Richard Nixon was the Sustaining Presence of only one member of the test group. This was a lady operator of a chain of supermarkets in Nebraska whose confidence was completely restored by an eighteen-hour daily application of Mr. Nixon's eloquent "Checkers Speech" of the 1952 Presidential campaign.

Senator Barry Goldwater was the Sustaining Presence of five members of the test group. A strong supporter of Dr. McLandress' work, the Senator came personally to the clinic to record sample extracts from his speeches and books. Governor Rockefeller, for whom Dr. McLandress had high hopes, proved surprisingly unpredictable as a Presence. Three members of the test responded well to recordings of his earlier speeches calling for an all-out nationwide program of fallout-shelter building. When, however, his views on taxes, economic growth, education and religion were substituted, the positive effect was no longer marked. Dr. McLandress suggests that if it is to serve as a Sustaining Presence, the Rockefeller personality must have careful editing.

In the end a Sustaining Presence was found for 96 per cent of the test group. As indicated, the search was in some cases a time-consuming one. One executive was sustained only by the dual Presence of Herbert Hoover and J. Edgar Hoover. The Sustaining Presence of another executive was eventually found to be Franklin D. Roosevelt. Probed for an explanation in the light of the severe impairment he was suffering under Kennedy, his only clue was that his wife had reported hearing him mutter in his sleep, "Better the devil, you know."

The Confidence Machine will shortly be available in quantity. The White House is known to have in its possession a detailed interdepartmental paper recommending that, at the appropriate time, consideration be given to setting up machinery for program analysis of proposals providing that fitting and use be made obligatory for all executives of companies with assets in excess of $5,000,000. Confidence, the paper argues, is infectious; so, *pro tanto,* is a lack of confidence. However, this analogy to a communicable disease and hence to the case for compulsory vaccination is not strongly supported by the Public Health Service.

A second plan, devised by Dr. McLandress himself, is to give every executive earning more than $25,000 annually a tax-free credit of 20 per cent of net taxable income if he obtains and uses a properly fitted Confidence Machine. This is a substantial incentive; an executive in the $100,000 range will have additional tax-free income of around $15,000 as a result. "With this inducement," Dr. McLandress told this reporter a few weeks ago, "we would strike at the very foundations of the problem of business confidence."

Allston Wheat's Crusade

IN THE field-house locker room of a large Midwestern university, a tall, serious-looking boy has just shaken hands with a little group of team mates and is saying goodbye to the coach. The coach holds the boy's hand for a moment and pleads with him. The boy shakes his head, squares his shoulders a trifle, and walks slowly out the door. There is a sequel next morning. Students stare at the headlines on the university daily:

CAI CLAIMS ANOTHER AT STATE

BREJENSKI TURNS IN UNIFORM, LEAVES SQUAD

This scene hasn't been enacted as yet. But the day is not distant when it may be commonplace. For a crusade is in the making to convince America that team sports are subverting her youth. It is still too early to say whether it will succeed. If it does, it will plunge organized athletics into the most serious crisis of its existence. Men who have never heard of Karl Marx, who consider Joseph Stalin another troublemaker now safely with the majority, and who find the baseball averages rather high mathematics will be involved in one of the hardest political, philosophical, and ethical decisions of the decade.

The man who is sounding the tocsin is a solidly built, kindly-appearing Pennsylvanian with sharp blue eyes and an urbane self-assured manner who, despite a tendency to slight corpulence, carries himself with the easy grace of the athlete he once was. His name is Allston C. Wheat and until a few months ago his fame rested on having been one of the best tennis players ever graduated from Cornell and on a subsequent career as a wholesaler of ethical drugs, antibiotics and rubber drug sundries in Philadelphia. He retired from business a few years ago when his company passed into the ownership of a chain of wholesale druggists and he now lives with his divorced daughter and two grandchildren in Haverford.

The termination of his business career gave "All" Wheat, as he was called in his tennis days, the time to catch up on the reading which he had been forced to neglect as an active businessman. He delved into the works of Jeremy Bentham, Ludwig von Mises, Henry Hazlitt, William Buckley, Dr. Herschel McLandress, Ayn Rand, the National Association of Manufacturers, the American Medical Association, and Senator Barry Goldwater. He also made a full collection of the advertisements on social and economic policy of the Warner and Swasey Corporation and began to take serious interest in movements designed to alert America to the menace of domestic socialism and communism. This study and experience provided him, he has since said, with the basic insights for understanding the world of sport. These he presented in his thoughtful and plain-spoken pamphlet, "The Menace of the Team," which has been called the Bible of his movement.

Allston Wheat's case against team sports is regularly cited by his admirers as an example of the powerful and logical mind of the modern conservative leader at work. The following quotations are from "The Menace of the Team" unless otherwise indicated:

> America, as we know it, was built on the system of individual free enterprise. Under that system, every individual stands on his own two feet, shoulders his own burdens, and fights his way to the top by his own two-fisted efforts.
>
> American individualism means that the individual is guided by his own self-interest. He is not responsible for, or to, others. He is responsible for, and to, himself. He knows that because some win in the game of life, some must lose. He is out to win. He is not concerned with what happens to those who lose. Nor does he want to be.
>
> The individualist is his own boss. He does not take orders from any commissar or bureaucrat. He is answerable only to himself. What he gets he keeps.
>
> These are the principles of American individualism. But do we train our people in these principles? *We do not.* We consciously and deliberately train the youth of our nation in

principles that are completely opposed to the spirit of American individualism.

Every healthy able-bodied young American is encouraged to participate in organized athletic sports — to play on a team. There he is indoctrinated with the team spirit. This tells him to think not of himself but of the other players. It tells him he must not shine at the expense of others, for if he does so he is a bad team player. It tells him that he must always back up the other players, be responsible for them, do what they fail to do. He learns it is the team that wins, not the man. If there is a prize or reward, it goes not to the man but to the team. The team is the social group which always comes

first. Society comes first, the individual last. At every point the young American is schooled against individualism. At every point team sports indoctrinate him in the principles and practices of collectivism and socialism.

Nor is this all. The team player is taught that he must accept without question the commands of the coach, captain or quarterback. He must bow to the authority of the group or accept the consequences. This is authoritarianism and since he must comply completely with the voice of authority, it is also totalitarianism. If a man has been schooled in totalitarianism on a sandlot or in the Yale Bowl or even as a spectator at the Yankee Stadium, is he likely to resist it in real life?

America is a country of team sports. We must see these sports for what they are. They are brainwashing stations for individualism. They are the training schools for collectivism, socialism, authoritarianism and totalitarianism.

* * * * * * *

If you are looking for the real advance guard for modern Communism, you should go to the field-houses and the football stadiums.[1]

Documenting his case, Allston Wheat shows that the great expansion in team sports — football, basketball, baseball, volleyball, hockey — has taken place in the last forty years or since World War I. Thus, its rise coincides almost exactly with the rise of socialism, communism, welfarism, and other forms of collectivism since the Russian Revolution. It would be naïve, he insists, to imagine that the two movements are unrelated.[2]

In fact, Allston Wheat thinks our entanglement in collec-

[1] The last quotation is from an address by Mr. Wheat entitled, "Athletics and Americanism" given at the Workshop on Athletic Individualism, University of Greater Dallas, January 22-31, 1961.

[2] The parallel is, in fact, even more striking. In 1867 the first rules for college football were drawn up in Princeton, New Jersey. That was the year of the publication of *Das Kapital.* The National League (originally the National League of Professional Baseball Clubs) was organized just nine years later. Basketball was invented in 1891 and the Socialist Labor Party ran its first candidate for President in the following year.

tivist athletics was a well-planned operation. Like most other collectivist ideas, team sports originated in the Ivy League colleges. Some Ivy League intellectuals certainly saw with considerable clarity what the role of team sports would be. Wheat especially notes the conclusions of Professor Barton Wheeler some fifty years ago in his book, *The Social Instinct*, as proof of this point:

> Although the higher anthropoids derive pleasure from each other's company and form themselves readily enough into social groups, until we get to man himself we find them deficient in the instinct to social cooperation. While they can be taught simple games, vide the baseball game made familiar by apes at the circus, there is no evidence of such play as a *form of social skill* or as a spontaneous manifestation of enjoyment. The reason is that a game is a highly developed social phenomenon involving *a complex commitment to interdependence and a highly developed capacity for providing and accepting leadership. These social qualities are developed only at a relatively advanced state in man.*[3]

Wheat thinks that what was clear to Professor Wheeler in 1911 was surely evident to other professors before and since. "Harvard introduced the ideas of Marx and Keynes to the United States," he says in "The Menace of the Team." "Why, therefore, should it draw the line at collectivist sports? The modern socialist state and modern collectivist athletics are both founded on the same fundamental idea, namely the subordination of the individual to the group — or mob."

In Allston Wheat's view, the individual's instinctive reaction to athletics is a precise index of his attitudes toward

[3] Beacon Hill Press, Boston, 1911. Italics added.

collectivism.[4] He scoffs at the idea that Dwight D. Eisenhower was either a conscious or an unconscious agent of the Communist conspiracy. Eisenhower showed his instinctive individualism by his preference for a strongly individualist game, namely golf. Many conservative businessmen and Republicans react naturally in the same way. Liberals have never liked golf. Herbert Hoover showed his extreme individualism

[4] Mention may be made here of the use which Wheat makes of the work of Dr. Herschel McLandress, the famed Boston psychometricist. Dr. McLandress has shown that successful participants in team sports have a McL–C that is substantially higher than that of most other celebrities. The McL–C or McLandress Coefficient measures the intensity of the individual's reaction to self; the lower the coefficient, the higher the intensity. Wheat, who has checked his conclusions carefully with Dr. McLandress to whom he frankly acknowledges a major debt, considers the McL–C to be a good index of individualism.

by his preference for fishing — a sport which requires neither another player nor a companion. Franklin D. Roosevelt, by contrast, went sailing with a crew and, very significantly, insisted on being the captain. The Kennedys showed from the very outset by their impromptu games of touch football that they are collectivist to the core. Nelson Rockefeller, he predicts, will show up in the baseball bleachers and at football games and otherwise play for the collectivist vote.

"Ideas are all very well," Allston Wheat has said, "but to alert America to the menace of collectivism, there is no alternative to effective organization." Following the publication of "The Menace of the Team," he invited a group of like-minded patriots to meet with him to formulate a program of practical action. Over a dozen answered the call and the fruit of nearly a week of arduous planning and discussion at French Lick, Indiana, early last year was the decision to launch the Crusade for Athletic Individualism, now popularly known as CAI. The aim of CAI is a comprehensive educational program on the dangers of team sports, or as the French Lick Congress declared in its Call to Action, "The lifting of the storm warnings on the collectivist training of our youth in the principles of socialist athletic cooperation."

No one in CAI minimizes the difficulty of the task. Other collectivist ideas — social security, socialized medicine, consumer cooperatives, publicly-owned utilities, government-owned communication satellites, farm price control, post exchanges, new TVA's — have been successfully attacked and their advocates have been exposed. But collectivist athletics have gone largely unnoticed.[5] It will not be easy to awaken people to their danger. Nevertheless, it is Allston Wheat's conviction that the American people invariably respond to any danger that is effectively presented.

The Communist Party has always placed its principal accent on youth. So, according to Allston Wheat, have the sponsors of collectivist athletics. And so will the Crusade for Athletic Individualism. Present plans call for an organization, called a Cell for Individualist Athletics, in every sizable American community and in every high school, junior high school, preparatory school, college, university, and at West Point, Annapolis, and the Air Force and Coast Guard Academies. "You may depend on it," Allston Wheat has said in a recent address inaugurating the Yale University Cell, "wherever sports for our youth are organized, we will be organized." Wheat's first great triumph occurred two months ago when two Army divisional commanders, responding to his appeal, abolished all collectivist athletics in their commands. Their action was warmly endorsed by Congressional supporters of Wheat's Crusade who have warned Secretary of Defense McNamara against any effort to withdraw "The Menace of the Team" from the list of approved pamphlets for Army orientation programs.

In most American communities, the Crusade will concentrate initially on the Little Leagues. In Allston Wheat's view, if an eight- or ten-year-old can be sufficiently indoctrinated with the team spirit and the habit of submission to group

[5] Not everyone was fooled. For many years J. Edgar Hoover has been an habitué of Toots Shor's and "21." Many supposed it was because he liked the sporting company. It is Wheat's view that he had more serious business in mind.

authority, he will become the finished raw material of collectivism for life. He says in "The Menace of the Team," "No ten-year-old who has been taught that he must submit to the authority of the team and that all glory accrues to the team will ever again be an unadulterated individualist." Wheat notes that the Little Leagues are a modern development and that our forefathers would never have thought of organizing children into teams. "They are the product of the same period and the same paternalist thinking that brought us the Welfare State. In my book, there is very little difference between the man who destroys the individualist character of our children and the man who molests them in a park."

In the colleges, the Crusade for Athletic Individualism will work closely with Young Americans for Freedom and the Intercollegiate Society for Individualists. Together, CAI, YAF and ISI hope to bring coaching staffs into the same line of critical fire that has hitherto been concentrated on socialist and other semi-subversive professors. There is no intention of interfering with established traditions of academic freedom and tenure. But it is believed that if the position of the coach can be made intrinsically uncomfortable and less remunerative, many of the more dangerous men will be driven from the profession. "One must suit the means to the ends," Allston Wheat has said. "The coaches are the training cadres of athletic collectivism."

However, the principal effort will be to enroll athletes in CAI which, of course, means their immediate withdrawal from team sports. A number of colleges and universities — the University of Southern California, Notre Dame, Georgia

Tech, Swarthmore, Harvard, Ohio State, Brandeis — are expected to meet this step by requiring promising young athletes to sign pledges at the time of their recruitment that they will not join CAI. Allston Wheat has strongly denounced these "yellow dog contracts." [6]

One important function of Wheat and his followers will be advising corporations on their recreation and athletic pro-

[6] He has had a measure of support in this from the Harvard and Stanford Law Schools. Writing in a forthcoming issue of the *Harvard Law Review*, a visiting West Coast professor has said that the pledges "may well raise questions related to the enforceability of contracts that are against public purpose . . . The ghosts of Norris and LaGuardia are hovering unpleasantly in the wings."

grams. Many large firms — General Motors, General Electric, General Dynamics, General Mills, General Baking, General Telephone, General Aniline and Film, International Shoe — have used team sports in their company recreation programs or have encouraged their dealers to sponsor teams or have given moral support to team sports in their communities. This means, according to Wheat, that they have been unconsciously indoctrinating their executives, employees, and customers in the ideas of collectivist cooperation and leadership.

> General Motors would never allow the organization of its younger executives into Production Brigades, Communes, Stakhanovist Groups, Work Cooperatives, or Industrial Shock Troops. It knows that these ideas belong to the Russians and the Red Chinese. Yet it encourages athletic teams which are constructed on exactly the same principles. Both insist on the absolute supremacy of the group over the individual and of socialist achievement as compared with individual achievement . . . The modern American corporation — deploying as it does great resources in money and manpower — is the natural defender of individualism. It should be the leader in the fight against collectivist indoctrination on the playing fields. It has not yet begun to shoulder its mandate.[7]

Industrial firms have responded well to the CAI appeal. A number have dropped their recreation programs or revised them to exclude team sports. One large Delaware corporation has retained Allston Wheat as its recreation consultant. Word

[7] Both quotations are from "Making Your Recreation Program Both Physically and Morally Healthy: A Handbook for Industrial Executives." Crusade for Athletic Individualism, Haverford, Pennsylvania, 1961, $1.75.

was quietly passed at the last meeting of the Congress of Industry of the National Association of Manufacturers that responsible and patriotic executives should henceforth set a good public example in their own recreational activities.

There remains the problem of the public. In the old days, Allston Wheat notes, it was the policy of the Communists to charge admission to their big rallies in Madison Square Garden. Many non-Communists went to see the show. But their dollars went to help finance the Communist conspiracy. "There is no such thing as an innocent spectator," says Wheat. "Dollars that nourished collectivism at Madison Square Garden can also nourish it at the Yankee Stadium and the Yale Bowl."

It is plain, nonetheless, that educating the American public against attendance at athletic events will be a long and slow process. Allston Wheat has rejected proposals for picketing and also for a boycott of the products of firms sponsoring team sports on television. ("Is your razor the instrument of the collectivist conspiracy?" was one of the slogans proposed.) These measures could cost the Crusade needed support, and there is some doubt about the legality of a boycott. Wheat has repeatedly warned his more enthusiastic followers to stay within the law, and last summer he personally reprimanded a Jackson, Mississippi, cell which had raided a number of sand-lots in the city and confiscated and destroyed balls, bats, gloves, and uniforms and in one park set fire to the bleachers and backstop.

CAI has other problems to solve. In Washington last summer Attorney General Robert F. Kennedy gave an off-the-record denunciation of the organization that for vehemence startled even seasoned Washington reporters. It developed during the questioning that he was under the impression that CAI opposed all forms of physical exercise. In fact, it makes a careful distinction between those sports where the individual submerges himself in the socialist environment of the team and accepts authoritarian direction from a captain or some other control apparatus and those such as swimming, diving, boxing, wrestling and squash where he is on his own. These

latter sports may even nurture individualism and the spirit of individual enterprise. Allston Wheat points out that many of his crusaders are graduates of the enterprise sports[8] and reminds audiences that CAI Vice President Timothy Jeffers once went eight rounds with the late Floyd Bennett. Wheat is also proud of his own tennis days although he concedes that, strictly speaking, the brilliant net play for which he is remembered would be partly ruled out by his ban on doubles.

His other problem is the exceedingly well-heeled character of his opposition. "Every person who passes through the turnstiles is an unwitting tool of this collectivist conspiracy, for he adds something to its fighting fund."

Texas money is beginning to come in. Also large corporations, Wheat feels, will soon see the need for backing individualism with dollars. Workshops on athletic individualism will be held this coming winter in Los Angeles, Oakland, Indianapolis, and Midland, Texas. Still Allston Wheat stresses the need for enlightened mass financial support: "The collectivists will fight with all they have. Those of us who are waging this battle will give generously of our time. We can only hope that the millions of Americans who have a stake in this struggle will be as generous with their money."

In a more intimate mood, Allston Wheat has analyzed the financial prospect. "There are, we estimate, about a half-million people in this country who can be taken by a move-

[8] In "The Menace of the Team," Wheat advocates the use of the term "enterprise sports" to distinguish these activities from the team sports. He also strongly protests references to tennis, boxing, wrestling, table tennis, squash and track "teams." These are not teams in the usual sense of that word. Rather they are individual athletes who for reasons of convenience travel and compete in company. They might more accurately be called "consortiums."

ment such as ours. In the past year or two, they have been hit pretty hard by the Birchers, the Christian Crusade, the National Indignation boys, the Katanga Freedom Fighters, and the rest. And some of the best gulls will think that we are pretty far out. Still, I am predicting a pretty damn good score."

The Takeover

As THE United States approached the mid-sixties, it would have been hard to think of a country in which the social system was seemingly more secure. The word "capitalism" had ceased to be pejorative. Free enterprise was praised by many professional proletarians. There was unemployment but the unemployed, unlike the Negroes, no longer went in for disturbing demonstrations or inconvenient demands. The membership of the Communist Party, after allowing for the agents of the Federal Bureau of Investigation who had joined in order to watch its proceedings, had reached a new low. By thoughtful scholars this was related to the Gross National Product which, adjusted for changes in the price level, had reached a new high. Yet historians may well say there was never a time when vigilance was more necessary or its absence more costly.

Among those who saw the danger were regrettably few from the law enforcement agencies. One who did, so far from being a detective, was a balding Massachusetts scientist and physician. His sensitively trained mind had also, in some measure, set in motion the chain of developments which, as he has since put it, "were to work a far from inconsiderable change in the more fundamental fabric of American society."

For years Dr. Herschel McLandress, the Boston psychometricist, has been the nation's leading student of quantitative aspects of human motivation and reaction. In the language of the layman, this means that he has been investigating the relation of cause to result in human behavior.

Much is known. The behavior of the individual human being is still highly unpredictable. One cannot tell what any particular person will do in response to a command, an insult, the fear of punishment or even with absolute certainty the prospect of profit. But, given well-studied experiences, mass behavior is quite predictable. If one knows, to resort again to simple and only slightly inaccurate language, the factors that are influencing a crowd, and if these factors have operated before, one can tell with high certainty how the crowd will behave again. Everyone has seen women at an outdoor party react to a summer shower. As a result, he knows almost instinctively what will happen when he feels the first few drops again.

There has remained the intensely practical problem of how to ascertain the factors that are influencing people at a given

time and how to establish in advance of the responding action (since there is no advantage in predictions that are made after the fact), what the response will be. But these problems have been coming within the range of modern sampling and computer techniques. By sampling, we can build up experience on the response to (say) a Berlin crisis, a newspaper strike or a speech by Dean Rusk. Then by modern computer methods, the behavior in response to a new crisis, strike or speech can be predicted with great promptness. The results *can be* highly accurate. The words *can be* must be emphasized for prediction is only possible if past experience is available to the memory drums of the computer. But more and more such experience — including responses to crises, strikes and official speeches — is becoming available.

In illustrating his methods in lectures at the Harvard Medical School, Dr. McLandress has often said that the best analogue is alcohol in an academic community. "How any given intellectual will react as the result of ingesting five martinis in fifty minutes is beyond the range of science. But the effect of similar consumption on the conversation, social aggressions or libido of any sizable group of known age composition, academic rank, sex, and social experience can be foretold with absolute accuracy." He likes to suggest, half seriously, that if the population profile and alcohol consumption at a faculty cocktail party could be telephoned to the Harvard-M.I.T. computer center at eight in the evening, he could by two minutes past eight have the exact pattern of conversation, argument and amatory advances at the party at nine.

It was certain that sooner or later Dr. McLandress would turn to the problem of predicting economic and business behavior. No other problem in behavioral science has received so much attention over so long a time and the reason is simple: Money is involved. If one can know in advance if businessmen will increase their investment in new manufacturing plant, buy more copper, tin or other nonferrous metals, spend more for advertising, increase the speed and horsepower of automobiles, buy common stocks, raise wages, raise steel prices, or slash the price of television sets, one can take the action which profitably anticipates these decisions. As a result,

the effort to predict business behavior has itself become a major business. To the desk of the alert entrepreneur each day now come a dozen financial journals, trade journals, market analyses, newsletters, confidential outlooks and plain business forecasts, all of which he studies in order to see how business will behave. This effort engages the extensive attention of the United States Government. The United States Department of Commerce, Department of Labor, Council of Economic Advisers and, on frequent occasions, even the President of the United States himself regularly undertake to analyze the economic outlook and tell what will happen.

Few men have been less interested in amassing a personal fortune than Herschel McLandress. But the paradox in the problem of forecasting business behavior was to him especially compelling. For obviously in spite of all the effort, business prediction remained unsuccessful. But were it to succeed, it would no longer be needed. For then the future would be certain, and no one can make a living forecasting the next sunrise. (Even the Weather Bureau, though its projections are still imperfect, has totally displaced the neighborhood weather prophet who told whether it would rain tomorrow.) Dr. McLandress was strongly attracted by the idea of eliminating uncertainty from business life and therewith, more than incidentally, the social oddity of a large and costly ateliar of business oracles who owed their existence not to their success but to their inadequacy.

Accordingly, in the late fifties, under a joint grant from the Ford Foundation, the Merrill Foundation for the Advancement of Financial Knowledge and the Estes Fund, Dr. McLandress launched a major study of the methodology and techniques of business forecasting. A panel of professors from the Department of Economics of the University of Chicago acted as his technical consultants on the intricacies of the free enterprise system. The prime dividend from this work was a series of lectures given under the suspices of the New York

Federal Reserve Bank in the late autumn of 1961. In these lectures Dr. McLandress developed a theoretical model for anticipating business decisions. It was a highly mathematical design and assumed a sophisticated knowledge of both modern psychometric methods and advanced computer techniques. Not many of those attending were able to follow the nuances of the McLandress argument. They displayed rapt attention nonetheless, and the lectures were much mentioned, even by those market analysts who were not wholly clear as to their content, in days following.

A few weeks after the Reserve Bank lectures, Dr. McLandress received a letter from a man in New York who said he had attended the lectures and had been stimulated, as a result, to do some work along similar lines. He asked for an appointment. His name, destined to be much better known before very long, was Benjamin Selig Smith. On the following Monday, the last patient had just departed when the visitor's taxi pulled up to the gap in the boxwood before the large red brick Edwardian house in Brighton, Massachusetts. Dr. McLandress had gone into a front room for a lounging jacket and saw the quietly dressed young man pay the driver, glance up and down the street and, for a moment, inspect the house before him. He then turned up the walk. There was something in the settled, aquiline, slightly humorless face of the young man which caught the attention of the watcher above. Dr. McLandress went down to open the door with the feeling that this was not to be an ordinary interview.

It was not. The two men talked for nearly two hours. Dr. McLandress invited his visitor to remain over for another talk the next day. It was evident before the end of the first conversation that Benjamin Selig Smith had devised a largely workable application of Dr. McLandress' system to the problem of business forecasting. For the two or three seemingly serious difficulties he had encountered, Dr. McLandress was able to offer comparatively straightforward solutions. At the second session, Dr. McLandress urged his visitor to try some simulated tests and if these proved out to go ahead with a trial run. Some investment would be required in the sampling system but computer time could be rented from I.B.M. Dr. McLandress thought that Smith would not be running a serious risk of financial loss if he applied his method to some practical problem in the securities, real estate or commodity markets on a modest scale. Dr. McLandress did not see Benjamin Selig Smith again.

He did continue on occasion to wonder about his visitor. Smith had been passionately interested in the problem of method and technique. And it was clear that he wanted to use the system once he was certain of its performance. But he did not seem to be concerned about money. Once or twice, almost with the air of a man making obeisance to the obvious, he observed that a successful application of the system would be "pretty profitable." Dr. McLandress has since said that, had the young man shown himself to have been primarily interested in profits, he would have given him short shrift. Yet his other and undefined preoccupations left Dr. McLandress with a faint sense of uneasiness.

Dr. McLandress next heard of Benjamin Selig Smith some months later from a State Street friend. There was, the latter happened to say, talk of a new wonder-boy on Wall Street. He had made a major killing on space age and missile stocks and some of the blue chips as well. Dr. McLandress surprised his friend by asking if the name was Smith. A few days later the same friend sent Dr. McLandress a clipping from the *Wall Street Journal.* It told of a new group of investors who were staking out "a major position" in the stock of New York and Chicago banks. "The name one hears," the item concluded, "is that of B. S. Smith." The next week, glancing through the back pages of *Newsweek,* Dr. McLandress' eye lit upon a line in an article entitled, "Consolidation in Chemicals": "Seasoned operators are impressed . . . the operation bears the trademark of Selig Smith." Then, a month later, Dr. McLandress' financial friend made another contribution, a copy of *Fortune* clipped open to "Businessmen in the News":

> Nothing so well suggests the vitality and regenerative powers of the system of free, private and individual enterprise than this new breed of young, calculating, competent and completely reticent operators . . . If anyone imagines that precision and audacity are without reward, let him with due allowances for Wall Street's love of drama contemplate the recent career of Benjamin Selig Smith . . . Texas oils . . . western range lands . . . the long neglected textile industry . . . rumors of a new move in insurance.

Dr. McLandress found himself revising his conclusion that the intense young man who had called on him on that March day was indifferent about money.

*

Then for a while Benjamin Selig Smith seemed very much in the news. Several of his deals, notably his moves on non-ferrous metals, utilities and steel, made the front page of *The Times. Newsweek* and *Time* had him in a manner of speaking on their covers — the subject was not available for interview and both magazines were forced to use paintings based on an old photograph from the *Yale News.* Both gave vivid accounts of his ascent in the financial world. Smith was also invited to present his views on tax reduction before

the House Ways and Means Committee but declined through an intermediary. He was named one of the ten outstanding young men of the year by the United States Chamber of Commerce but did not accept the award in person. He did accept, *in absentia,* the Blough medal for industrial statesmanship. He was offered a place on the Business Advisory Council of the United States Department of Commerce and on a committee studying the administration of foreign aid. He declined both. Clearly he did not seek the floodlights.

Smith was also singled out for attack in the Senate of the United States by Senator Estes Kefauver who called for steps "to contain what might well be a malicious march toward monopoly." Kefauver's attack evoked an eloquent defense of Smith from Ohio legislators in whose state the Smith interests had staked out an important position in bituminous coal, steel and iron ore and from Senator Everett McKinley Dirksen who, it was thought, sensed an attack on the packing industry and Illinois Central Railroad, both of which were said to be pivots of the Smith position in Illinois. After a heated debate, a motion to investigate the Smith operations was voted down by a coalition of Republicans and middle-of-the-road Democrats. Some of the latter, while not opposing the motion in principle, expressed their reluctance at seeing any new harassment of business. Senator Barry Goldwater, defending Smith, stressed his very strong belief that this was no time for compromise with socialism. "Let us always beware of those who would hobble the free enterprise system by attacking, under whatever guise, its most dynamic practitioners. Success is not un-American."

In recent months, however, Benjamin Selig Smith has largely disappeared from the news. Outside of the financial community, such is the public memory, few will now recognize the name. The newspapers have continued to carry the warnings of Senator Goldwater and others against any interference with individual liberty. But there has been little mention of Smith. A Department of Justice proposal to look into the affairs of the Smith combine ran into a strongly adverse editorial reaction and was hastily dropped. Smith himself has become an even more ethereal figure than before. He did not attend a testimonial dinner given in his honor by the former officers of Morgan-Guaranty Trust on the occasion of the final New York bank consolidation. He did not attend the Fortieth Anniversary dinner of *Time* Magazine and declined an invitation to speak at the Calvin Bullock Forum. In addition to the quickly aborted Department of Justice investigation, there have been rumors that the Federal Trade Commission, the Securities and Exchange Commission, the Interstate Commerce Commission and the Federal Communications Commission had doubts about the Smith operations. These

led to the strong warnings against "unwarranted government interference with legitimate private enterprise" at the last annual Congress of Industry of the National Association of Manufacturers. The press strongly echoed these protests. So did the United States Chamber of Commerce and the Daughters of the American Revolution. Governor Nelson Rockefeller came out vigorously in support of "the new spirit exemplified by the new and dynamic forces now invigorating the American

economy." In an addendum, which was not widely reported, he denied that the Rockefeller family was borrowing heavily from the Smith interests.

When the name of Benjamin Selig Smith dropped from the public news, it did not pass entirely from Dr. McLandress' mind. He continued to hear from his State Street friend of big operations in the financial community. Prices and property values seemed to be somewhat in flux; men of means were said to be experiencing rapid changes in their asset position and Dr. McLandress' friend confessed that he was feeling the wind himself. The name of Smith was passed from lip to lip in connection with these changes and came occasionally to Dr. McLandress' ear. However, the community at large heard little and the government had come to take a benign view of the situation. At the end of the year, the President's Council of Economic Advisers looked with approval on the gains of the previous period and with confidence at the prospect. This confidence was echoed in bank letters, investment analyses, statements of business leaders and the annual financial survey of *The New York Times*. Although no knowledgeable person any longer questioned the importance of Benjamin Selig Smith, he remained silent as usual.

Some four weeks ago, Dr. McLandress had a second visitor.

The second visitor who came up the walk in Brighton was in marked contrast with the first. Dr. McLandress put aside the *Boston Herald* — an editorial sharply attacking the Chinese Communist leaders, another suggesting that the farm problem could not be solved without a drastic consolidation

of small inefficient units — and opened the door to a slight, rather furtive man with the vaguely purple complexion of the problem drinker. He responded almost too quickly when Dr. McLandress asked him if he would "have something." With a glass in his hand, he settled down to tell his story.

His name was Derwit Mather. He had been, for a brief period, a roommate of Benjamin Selig Smith's at Yale and had gone on after graduation to take a Ph.D. in mathematics and mathematical statistics. He had taught for a time at Swarthmore and had lost his job. (Dr. McLandress thought of the drinking.) Badly in need of employment, he was offered a job by his old friend and had worked on problems of programming financial data for a Univac. He was not in Benjamin Selig Smith's confidence but over a period of time he had developed a shrewd idea of what was going on. Some of this was hardly news to Dr. McLandress.

From his system Smith could, in fact, derive exact information on what was going to happen in any market to which he turned. Initially he simply used this foresight to be long in the stock market whenever it went up and short whenever it went down, with the appropriately different position in stocks that resisted or reversed the trend. Similarly whenever commodity prices rose, Smith would be in; whenever they tumbled, he was out and ready to buy back in at the bottom. These early operations aroused no suspicion on the part of Mather. Smith paid Mather well and, Dr. McLandress gathered, closed his eyes to the occasional bouts with the bottle.

Nor was Mather immediately suspicious when Smith launched into the second phase of his operations. In this stage he used the ample returns from the first phase to acquire a major interest in several of the nation's larger corporations. The technique was simple. Having taken an initial position, he launched a bull movement to drive up the stock with a view to encouraging all those attracted by capital gains to sell. Then after a major bear raid, he bought from those who were discouraged by low prices. In this operation, Smith had not only eliminated uncertainty for himself but had greatly increased it for everyone else. His market activities made him all the money he needed for these operations. In the operations themselves he could not lose and almost everyone else was certain to lose.

According to Mather, when Smith hit his stride, he was moving in on major firms at the rate of four or five a day. To

stake out a position in the whole economy was less time-consuming than might have been imagined. Some seven or eight hundred large corporations account for the majority of the industrial, mercantile, financial, transportation and public utility assets of the United States, and Smith worked from a ready-made list which had been published by *Fortune* Magazine in the previous July. In a little more than a hundred days, Smith had taken giant strides toward control of the major enterprises of the nation. Mather thought Smith had been troubled by the considerable publicity which had attended the early phases of his operations. This explained the high priority which he had assigned to the newspaper chains, the major metropolitan papers, the news magazines and the three major broadcasting chains.

A third phase of Smith's operations involved the liquidation of two stubborn problems. First there were the hold-outs — the scattered Du Ponts, Murchisons and Humphreys who could not be conned or compelled into selling their property. And there was the obvious fact that those who had been induced to sell would have the money which Benjamin Selig Smith had given them for the property. This might tempt them to buy back in. Smith wanted both property and money. To get them, according to Mather, he had devised a double envelopment or whipsawing strategy. Suspending all investment expenditure by all of the corporations he controlled, he could thereby bring about a drastic deflation of production, profits, prices and property values. This could be carried to the point where even the most stubborn men of property would have no choice but to sell if they were to continue to eat and maintain anything approaching their accustomed standard of living. Then, reversing the process, Smith could double, treble and quadruple expenditure. This would bring about an inflation which would render valueless all money remaining in the hands of those who had sold out to Smith. At this stage, farm, household and smaller shopkeepers' goods apart, Smith would be in full possession. Smith was already engaged in a preliminary whipsawing of the economy. In the weeks ahead he could be counted upon to step it up in both momentum and violence. Dr. McLandress could not help reflecting that already there had been a considerable falling off among his wealthier clients.

It had been late afternoon when Mather called. The room had grown dark as he talked and as he finished, Dr. McLandress got up and turned on the light. He noticed for the first time the look of weariness and strain on his visitor's face.

"I had to hitchhike here," Mather said. "It's years since I have done that sort of thing. The building janitor called the office to say I was feeling pretty unwell — that has happened before — but I think word has gone out. Busy signals from all the airlines. He has the phone company, you know.

"You may wonder how I learned about this last phase. This was left in the private washroom day before yesterday." Mather handed Dr. McLandress a thickish Modern Library book in blue-green binding from which protruded a number of slips of paper. He pulled out a slip. "This one has your name and address. I always thought he might have drawn on you in working out the system. Here is another. 'Capitalist crisis.' It outlines the technique of expropriation through the deflation-inflation ploy. And here is a 'Note for orderly execution of last step.' 'Need for strong hand at helm to meet crisis. Newspaper demand for appointment as Secretary of Treasury. Approval from press. Obvious conflict of interest. All property gifted to Government. Treasury as custodian. Expropriation accomplished. Revolution bloodless, complete. Denunciation China, Albania. Castro? Warsaw Pact?' "

"Don't overlook the underlined passages in the book: They do spell it out in advance."

Dr. McLandress followed Mather's finger along first one and then another heavily underscored line. The words, faintly familiar from some distant lectures, perhaps in Edinburgh, looked out from the page.

> One capitalist always kills many . . . centralization of the means of production and socialization of labor at last reaches the point where they become incompatible with their capitalist integument. This integument is burst asunder. The knell of capitalist private property sounds.

Dr. McLandress walked over to the window and looked out at the gray, brown and dark slate of the Boston winter landscape. The view met and merged with his mood. In an adjacent room, a television set burst into sound. For a few moments small swatches of voice, engaged in scholarly debate, came into the room. WGBH. Someone important from Harvard? The editor of the *Christian Science Monitor*? "There is much in what you say . . . Noninterference . . . Vital principle . . . Reward enterprise, not penalize . . . Principle . . . A very great deal in what . . ."

Someone turned the set to a discreet whisper or shut it off.